The U.S. Health Industry

THE COSTS OF ACCEPTABLE
MEDICAL CARE BY 1975

Edward Yost

PRAEGER SPECIAL STUDIES IN
U.S. ECONOMIC AND SOCIAL DEVELOPMENT

The U.S. Health Industry

THE COSTS OF ACCEPTABLE MEDICAL CARE BY 1975

Edward Yost

FREDERICK A. PRAEGER, Publishers
New York • Washington • London

The purpose of the Praeger Special Studies is to make specialized research monographs in U.S. and international economics and politics available to the academic, business, and government communities. For further information, write to the Special Projects Division, Frederick A. Praeger, Publishers, 111 Fourth Avenue, New York, N.Y. 10003.

FREDERICK A. PRAEGER, PUBLISHERS
111 Fourth Avenue, New York, N.Y. 10003, U.S.A.
5, Cromwell Place, London S.W.7, England

Published in the United States of America in 1969
by Frederick A. Praeger, Inc., Publishers

Library of Congress Catalog Card Number: 69-19352

Printed in the United States of America

DEDICATED TO MY FATHER

EDWARD F. YOST

IN MEMORIAM

PREFACE

During the late fall of 1966, Professor Seymour Melman, of Columbia University, directed my attention to the growing crisis in the health care of Americans. He was particularly concerned with the disparity that exists between the health services available to the affluent middle-class Americans and the medical treatment available to the poor.

Since we are both engineers, our viewpoint in examining the provision of a socio-economic service to the nation was to regard health as an industry. The analysis contained herein focuses on the current state of the nation's health industry as an alternative-cost study utilizing industrial engineering techniques. My objective is to establish the capital and operating investment in people, facilities, and money to bring the output of health services to meet a particular level of performance. Obviously, different levels of medical care, as well as different levels of availability to society, require distinctly different levels of investment.

One essential feature of this study must be called to the reader's attention. In extrapolating the investment required to provide a given amount of health care by 1975, it is assumed that both the social and the technological arrangements for the rendering of health services will not be subjected to cataclysmic change. It is assumed that the physician will remain primarily self-employed (except when attaching himself to a hospital as a resident), that medicine will not be nationalized, and that medical instrumentation will supplement but not replace the need for people. The fundamental position is that it takes a person to care for another person; apparatus, no matter how sophisticated, is an adjunct to this human relationship.

The data upon which this study is based has been provided by the U.S. Department of Health, Education and Welfare and the American Medical Association, as well as numerous professional health societies, which are referred to throughout the work. A particular note of thanks is due to The Physicians Forum, who initiated this work by a special grant.

CONTENTS

Page

Chapter   Page

LIST OF TABLES

TABLES IN THE APPENDIXES

Appendix A

The U.S. Health Industry

THE COSTS OF ACCEPTABLE
MEDICAL CARE BY 1975

Edward Yost

CHAPTER **1** INTRODUCTION

This study on the condition of the nation's health and the health industry has been conducted to answer the following three questions:

1. What is the cost in money, manpower, and physical units (schools, hospitals, etc.) to continue the present level of medical care, with existing variations, allowing for projected population growth to 1975? In other words, what change in outlay is required to keep the present standards of medical care?

2. What is the cost of a comprehensive health service for all U.S. citizens equal to that currently available in middle-class geographical areas?

3. What change in outlay is required to supply all U.S. citizens with those medical services currently available to affluent middle-class American families?

In order to answer these questions, it is necessary to establish what the present level of medical care in the United States is and the variations that exist in this level of care.

THE CONDITION OF THE NATION'S HEALTH

A survey concluded in June, 1967, found that over 96 million people in the United States suffered from chronic ill health. This represented almost 50 per cent of the population of the entire nation. More

than 72 per cent of the population between forty-
five and sixty-four years of age and 86 per cent of
persons sixty-five years and older have chronic
health conditions.

Chronic ill health and income are closely related. It cannot be stated with confidence which is
the cause and which is the effect (that is, does
chronic ill health cause a low income-producing capa-
bility or is a low income a factor in producing ill
health?). However, the consequences of chronic illness are catastrophic for low-income families. Almost
11 per cent of persons who belong to family units
having an income of $3,000 or less suffer a major
limitation in ability to work, keep house, or go to
school. An additional 4 per cent are unable to car-
ry on any major activity. This percentage is three
times that found in families with incomes of $10,000
or more. The latest available data prior to enactment of Medicare legislation showed that only 34 per
cent of members of families with an income of $2,000
and less had some form of health insurance compared
to over 90 per cent for persons in families with an
income of $7,000 or more. Among persons who were
hospitalized, insurance covered some part of the bill
for 80 per cent of the patients in family units with
an income in excess of $7,000 but only 40 per cent
of patients in family units having less than $2,000
income. A person in a family with an income of
$2,000 and less had, on the average, sixteen more
days of restricted activity per year than a person
in a family with an income of $7,000 and more.

Of the total households in 1960, 12 per cent of
white and 57 per cent of nonwhite households had
family incomes of less than $3,000. This difference
in income is reflected as a difference in health between the white and nonwhite population. The life
expectancy of the nonwhite population in 1965 was 10
per cent less than that of the white population--64.5
years compared to 71.0 years. The number of maternal deaths per 100,000 population is four times as
large for the nonwhite as for the white population--
98.1 deaths compared to 24.4. The postneonatal*

---

*Twenty-eight days through eleven months.

deaths per 1,000 live births was 15.4 for the nonwhite population compared to 5.5 for the white population.

THE CONDITION OF THE HEALTH INDUSTRY

Manpower

The health industry currently employs 3.5 million
persons in all types of health-related activities.
Doctors, dentists, and nurses account for only slightly more than 1 million of the total.

There has been an increase in the total number of
physicians from 232,697 in 1950 to 322,045 in 1967.
The ratio of physicians to patient care per 100,000
civilians also increased from 125 in 1963 to 130 in
1967. In 1967, the ninety-four U.S. medical schools
graduated 8,148 physicians, almost 90 per cent of
whom were licensed to practice medicine.

During the 1960-65 period an average of 2,135
foreign-trained physicians were licensed each year
to practice medicine in the United States. Each year
the United States imports and licenses the equivalent
of the output of twenty-six U.S. medical schools.
An increase of 30 per cent in the number of medical
schools would be required if importation of foreign-
trained physicians were not permitted.

Low wages and poor working conditions in the
health industry are causing discontent and a high
labor turnover. In 1963, over 25 per cent of registered nurses earned less than $80 per week. In met-
ropolitan hospitals the average annual earnings of
nurses was $4,450, which was $2,000 less than the
average annual earnings for a teacher. Nearly 30 per
cent of hospital clerical staffs were earning less
than $60 per week. This can be compared to the av-
erage earnings for production workers in manufactur-
ing industries in 1965, which was $99.63 per week.

The situation is worse in nursing homes, where
30 per cent of all nonsupervisory workers earned less
than $1.00 per hour, and 62 per cent of service and

maintenance employees did not receive one full day
paid holiday during the year. On February 1, 1967,
the Fair Labor Standards Act established a minimum
wage of $1.00 per hour for workers in health insti-
tutions.

The health industry is loaded with dead-end jobs.
The possibility of a nurse's aide becoming a licensed
practical nurse is as remote as her becoming an M.D.

Facilities

In 1967, there were a total of 8,200 hospitals
in the nation with 1.6 million beds. Of these, 6,661
were nonfederal general hospitals with a total capacity of 796,140 beds. Thirty-seven per cent of these
beds do not conform to minimum federal standards because of safety and fire hazards. An additional
329,997 acceptable beds are required to bring the nation up to the minimum bed-population ratio thought
necessary in 1946, when the Hill-Burton hospital construction and modernization legislation was passed.
There is an average of 409 general hospital beds per
100,000 population. However, there is great varia-
bility by state in the number of general hospital beds
available per capita. For instance, in Alaska the
bed-population was 238 per 100,000, but the figure was
493 per 100,000 in Iowa.

In 1967, over one third of the nation's existing
long-term-care beds in hospitals and nursing homes
were classified as unacceptable by the Public Health
Service because of serious fire and/or safety hazards.
Less than half of the long-term-care beds classified
as conforming to federal standards and required under
the Hill-Burton Act were available in 1967. The bed
deficit is more than three times that of general hospitals.

In 1964, only 32 per cent of the 326 state and
local mental institutions in the entire country had
been approved by the Joint Commission on Accredita-
tions of Hospitals. Mental-hospital beds have increased only by 25 per cent between 1948 and 1965,
yet there was a simultaneous increase of 37 per cent

in the total population. This has resulted in a declining ratio of acceptable mental beds per 100,000
population from 275 in 1948 to 251 in 1965.

THE COST OF BETTER HEALTH CARE

In order to supply the nation with a minimal
level of health service in 1975, allowing for population growth, an additional capital investment of at
least $29 billion and a yearly operating cost of $5
billion will be required to provide the following:

(1) An additional 26 medical schools to sup-
    ply the 2,135 physicians the United
    States depletes from other societies by
    importation.

(2) Eight additional dental schools to pro-
    vide an additional 5,057 dentists to the
    estimated 1975 dentist population.

(3) Ninety-one additional schools of regis-
    tered nursing to satisfy the expected
    shortage of 2,817 nurses per year.

(4) A net addition of 120,020 general hospi-
    tal beds.

(5) A net addition of 520,859 mental hospital
    beds.

(6) A net addition of 232,969 long-term-care
    beds.

(7) A total of 1,884 diagnostic and treatment
    centers, 458 rehabilitation facilities,
    and 1,218 public health centers in addi-
    tion to those already in existence.

In order to evaluate the level of health services
available to an affluent segment of the population,
Westchester County, New York, was used as a sample
population. To bring the national level of health
care to equal that generally available to residents

of this county, whose average family income is
$13,440, an additional capital investment of $49 billion above the current level of expenditures and
yearly operating cost of at least $11 billion would
be required. This $49 billion capital investment
would provide:

> (1) An addition of 142 medical schools to
>   provide an increase of 12,374 physicians
>   per year.
>
> (2) An additional 770 schools of nursing to
>   provide 23,885 additional nurses per year.
>
> (3) An additional 194 dental schools to pro-
>   vide a yearly increase of 13,000 dentists.
>
> (4) A total of 421,954 more general hospital
>   beds.
>
> (5) An additional 303,763 mental-hospital beds.
>
> (6) An additional 375,094 long-term-care beds.
>
> (7) A total of 2,671 more diagnostic and
>   treatment centers, 474 additional rehabil-
>   itation facilities, and 1,677 additional
>   public health centers.

These needs for health facilities and personnel
underscore the fact that even the affluent middle-
class white American does not have adequate health
services as indicated by a plausible standard.

Estimates of the current capital investment in
medical facilities of all types vary from between
$2.3 and $3.1 billion for 1967. The projected capital outlay in 1975 is between $2.5 and $3.3 billion.
These figures include replacement and repair of existing facilities as well as construction of new
hospital beds and medical facilities. This capital
investment over the next eight years is for the most
part a fight against obsolescence.

It should be noted that the above figures per-
tain only to capital investments. In addition to any

capital investment, the current operating cost of
the nation's hospitals and medical education programs
is roughly estimated to be $11.9 billion per year.

Where will the money come from to make the large
capital investments that are required? If either of
the investments enumerated above resulted in improving the health of persons who are members of families
with incomes of $3,000 or less to equal that of mem-
bers of family units with incomes of $10,000 or more,
there would be an increase of at least $1.4 billion
in personal income per year. This is in addition to
the improved quality of life that would result. If
these effects of improved health are applied to members of families above the lowest level of income,
then the predicted gain to the nation would be at
least three times the above. Thus, the capital investment in health services suggested above are plausible using a commonly accepted rate of return on
business investments.

CHAPTER **2** THE STATE OF THE
NATION'S HEALTH

There are innumerable health indicators, such as
incidence of disease, infant mortality, longevity,
and so forth, which can provide an indication of the
physical health of a social group. Each indicator
has its particular advantages depending on the use
to which the information is to be put. In order to
provide a general indication of the health of the
population of the United States we have selected as
our primary health indicator <u>chronic health conditions
causing a limitation in activity</u>. Our hypothesis is
that this categorization of health will serve as an
indicator of the basic social condition of a population. In order for a society to be self-supporting
and capable of vigorous activity as a social entity,
a major portion of the population must be free from
chronic health limitations to their physical activity.
Those that are blessed with health form the dynamic
productive core of a society. Not only must this
core of healthy people provide the goods and services
required by the entire population, but they must also
care for those whom poor health has rendered unable
to care for themselves.

CHRONIC HEALTH CONDITIONS

During the twelve-month period from July, 1966,
to June, 1967, a health-interview survey of the civilian noninstitutional population of the United
States was conducted on a sample basis.[1] From this
survey it is estimated that of the population at that
time of 192,359,000 persons, 49.9 per cent, or
96,035,000 persons, were suffering from one or more
chronic health conditions. A slight difference in

chronic disorders appears between the sexes. Of the
female population, 51 per cent has one or more chronic health conditions compared with approximately 49
per cent of the males. The major difference in health
conditions appears to be related to age. Slightly
more than 23 per cent of the population under seven-
teen years of age suffer chronic ailments; this percentage increases to almost 45 per cent of the
seventeen-to-twenty-four age group, 59 per cent of
the twenty-five-to-forty-four age group, 72 per cent
of the forty-five-to-sixty-four age group, and 86 per
cent of the sixty-five and older group. A detailed
breakdown of the number and per cent of the population with one or more chronic health conditions by
sex and age is shown in Table 1.

An indication of the incidence of chronic health
condition in the United States according to color,
income, and sex is available from a national survey
conducted between July, 1965, and June, 1966.[2] The
per cent distribution of persons in these categories
by degree of limitation is shown in Table 2. These
data provide a significant indication of the nation's
health. While approximately 44 per cent of the nonwhite population is recorded as having one or more
chronic health conditions, almost 50 per cent of the
white population is so categorized. However, while
6.1 per cent of the white population is limited by
chronic health conditions in the amount or kind of
major activity (ability to work, keep house, or go
to school), 7.7 per cent of the nonwhite population
is so afflicted. These data indicate that the consequences of chronic health ailments in the nonwhite
population is somewhat more severe than in the white
population. The data also show that while there is
no drastic difference in the incidence of chronic
illness with race, the consequences of illness appear
catastrophic for low-income groups; 10.7 per cent of
persons belonging to family units having incomes of
less than $3,000 are limited in ability to work or
keep house or go to school (major activities). This
percentage decreases to 7.1 per cent in the $3,000 to
$5,000 family-income group; 5.8 per cent in the $5,000
to $7,000 group; 4.9 per cent in the $7,000 to $10,000
group; and 4.1 per cent of persons belonging to family
groups with $10,000 and over.

TABLE 1

Number and Percentage of Population with One or More Chronic Health Conditions by Sex and Age, United States, July, 1966–June, 1967

Sex and Age	Total Population (in thousands)	Persons with One or More Chronic Conditions	
		Number (in thousands)	Per Cent of Population
Both Sexes			
All Ages	192,359	96,035	49.9
Under 17 Years	67,001	15,564	23.2
17–24 Years	23,074	10,286	44.6
25–44 Years	45,149	26,713	59.2
45–64 Years	39,270	28,112	71.6
65 Years and Over	17,865	15,361	86.0
Male			
All Ages	92,802	45,235	48.7
Under 17 Years	34,080	8,379	24.6
17–24 Years	10,641	4,720	44.4
25–44 Years	21,515	12,276	57.1
45–64 Years	18,806	13,248	70.4
65 Years and Over	7,761	6,613	85.2

Female

All Ages	99,557	50,800	51.0
Under 17 Years	32,921	7,185	21.8
17-24 Years	12,433	5,566	44.8
25-44 Years	23,634	14,437	61.1
45-64 Years	20,465	14,863	72.6
65 Years and Over	10,104	8,748	86.6

Source: U.S. Department of Health, Education and Welfare, Public Health Service, "Current Estimates from the Health Survey, United States, July 1966-June 1967," Public Health Service Publication No. 1,000, Series 10, No. 43 (1968).

TABLE 2

Degree of Chronic Activity Limitation of Population According to Color,
Family Income, and Sex (Age-adjusted[a] Percentage Distribution)
United States, July, 1965-June, 1966

Characteristic	All Persons	Persons with no Chronic Conditions	Persons with One or More Chronic Conditions				
			Total	With No Limitation of Activity	With Limitation but Not in Major Activity[b]	With Limitation in Major Activity[b]	Unable to Carry on Major Activity[b]
Population-all ages	100.0	50.9	49.4	37.9	2.8	6.3	2.1
Color:							
White	100.0	50.2	49.8	38.9	2.9	6.1	2.0
Nonwhite	100.0	56.2	43.8	30.3	2.2	7.7	3.7
Family Income:							
Under $3,000	100.0	48.5	51.5	33.5	3.6	10.7	3.9
$3,000-4,999	100.0	52.1	47.9	35.8	2.7	7.1	2.7
$5,000-6,999	100.0	52.3	47.7	37.8	2.5	5.8	1.6
$7,000-9,999	100.0	50.9	49.1	40.0	2.8	4.9	1.4
$10,000+	100.0	49.8	50.2	41.8	3.0	4.1	1.3
Sex:							
Male	100.0	51.5	48.5	36.3	2.4	6.6	3.2
Female	100.0	50.4	49.6	39.2	3.2	6.1	1.1

[a]Adjusted to the age distribution of the total U.S. civilian noninstitutional population.
[b]"Major activity" refers to ability to work, keep house, or engage in school or preschool activities.

Source: U.S. Department of Health, Education and Welfare, Public Health Service, "Limitations of Activity and Mobility Due to Chronic Conditions, United States, July 1965-June 1966," Public Health Service Publication No. 1,000, Series 10, No. 45 (1968).

Similar data for the 1964-65 health-interview survey showed that there is a 10 per cent increase in chronic health affliction for the married segment of the population compared to those who remained single.[3] This health hazard is conveniently attributed to the age difference in the two groups rather than to the rigors of married life.

Another view on chronic activity limitation of the population is supplied by Table 3. Here it can be seen that the South has the distinction of having the largest percentage of the population suffering chronic limitations of activity in all age categories and the Northeast the least.

TABLE 3

Percentage of Population with Chronic
Limitations of Activity
(by Age and Geographic Region),
United States, July, 1963–June, 1965

Region	Per Cent of Population		
	Under 45 Years	45 to 64 Years	65 and Over
Northeast	3.9	14.3	39.8
North Central	4.9	19.3	47.8
South	5.9	25.4	59.6
West	5.4	20.0	46.6

Source: U.S. Department of Health, Education and Welfare, Public Health Service, "Health Characteristics by Geographic Region, Large Metropolitan Areas, and Other Places of Residence, United States, July 1963–June 1965."

Here we may ask, "What ailments are the causes of the limitations on the physical activity of the population?" Table 4 shows the per cent of persons reporting selected chronic conditions as causes of limitations. The data are derived by dividing the specific chronic condition causing limitations by

the total number of persons limited in activity. The
geographic differentials of health indicated in Table
3 are shown in latter data to be primarily due to
differentials in income and secondarily associated
with race differences.

TABLE 4

Percentages of Population Reporting Selected
Chronic Conditions as a Cause
of Limitation
July, 1963

Selected Chronic Conditions	Per Cent of Population Limited in Activity	
	White	Nonwhite
Heart Condition	16.4	13.6
Arthritis and Rheumatism	14.6	16.6
Impairment of Back or Spine (Except Paralysis)	7.6	7.1
Mental and Nervous Conditions	7.5	8.7
Impairments, Lower Extremities and Hips (Except Paralysis or Absence)	6.0	7.5
Hypertension (Without Heart Involvement)	5.5	9.7

Source: U.S. Department of Health, Education and
Welfare, Public Health Service, "Chronic Conditions
and Activity Limitations, United States, July 1963."

It is interesting to note that the data seem to
indicate noticeably greater chronic limitations due
to mental, nervous, and hypertension conditions in
the nonwhite population as compared to the white population. One wonders if this might be attributed to
social pressures stemming from discrimination?

WHITE-NONWHITE DIFFERENTIALS IN HEALTH

In 1964, there were 22.6 million nonwhites in the
United States. This comprised 11.8 per cent of the
total resident population. Negroes accounted for 91
per cent of the nonwhite population.

Of total households in 1960, 12 per cent of white
households and 57 per cent of nonwhite households had
a 1959 family income of less than $3,000. At the
other end of the income scale, 43 per cent of white
households and only 15 per cent of nonwhite households
had a family income of $7,000 or more.[4]

Measures of the U.S. level of living are sound
housing, hot piped water, and the availability of a
telephone and an automobile. In 1960, 72 per cent of
white households had these items compared with only
35 per cent of nonwhite households.[5]

Life expectancy for the nonwhite population in
1965 was approximately 10 per cent shorter than for
the white population (64.1 years and 71.0 years re-
spectively).[6]

Maternal and infant death rates are sensitive
socio-economic indicators of human well-being. In
1963, the number of maternal deaths per 100,000 live
births was 24.2 for the white population and 98.1 for
the nonwhite; 16.7 neonatal (under 28 days) deaths
per 1,000 live births for the white population and
26.1 for the nonwhite population; 5.5 post-neonatal
(28 days through 11 months) deaths for the white
population and 15.4 for the nonwhite.[7] However, it
should be noted that seven out of eight nonwhite
mothers were attended at birth by physicians in hospitals.[4]

Over the years the mortality among the nonwhite
population has been consistently higher for most
causes of death. Among the highest ratios of nonwhite to white mortality are tuberculosis, influenza,
pneumonia, and vascular lesions affecting the central
nervous system.[8]

Those health services used by a high percentage
of the population are a measure of utilization of
health services in general. With the current empha-
sis on preventive care, the volume of physician and
dental visits can be used as an indication of the
health status of the population, as both the sick and
the well use these services.[9]

From July, 1963, through June, 1964, the white
population recorded an average of 4.7 physician visits per person (over 770 million visits) compared
with an average of 3.3 visits per person among the
nonwhite group (72.6 million visits).* During the
period from July, 1966, through June, 1967, the white
population had an average of 4.5 physician visits per
person and the nonwhite population 3.1 visits per
person. Dental visits in the white population aver-
aged 1.7 per person per year and in the nonwhite population 0.9 visits per person per year. As can be
seen from Table 5, during the 1963-64 period the differences between the ratio of physician visits for
the white and nonwhite groups decreased as family income increased.

Viewed another way, about 67 per cent of the
white population and 56 per cent of the nonwhite population saw a doctor once in the year prior to the
1963-64 survey. As can be seen from Table 6, the
differential in rates of visits decreased as family
income rose, with the rate for whites ranging from
62 per cent among those with incomes of less than
$2,000 to 73 per cent of those with incomes of $10,000
or more, while the comparable range for nonwhites was
51 per cent to 67 per cent.

The proportion of whites who visited a dentist
at least once during the year prior to the interview

─────────────────

*A physician visit is defined as consultation
with a physician (or a nurse or technician acting
under his supervision) in person or by telephone for
examination, diagnosis, treatment, or advice, ex-
clusive of inpatient hospital care.

TABLE 5

Physician and Dental Visits, July, 1963–June, 1964

(in millions)

Family Income	Visits		Visits per Person per Year[a]			
			(Unadjusted)		(Age-adjusted)	
	White	Nonwhite	White	Nonwhite	White	Nonwhite
All Incomes[a]			*Physician Visits*			
	771.7	72.7	4.7	3.3	4.7	3.5
Under $2,000	74.3	18.5	4.9	2.9	4.6	3.5
$2,000–3,999	109.5	21.0	4.6	3.4	4.5	3.9
$4,000–6,999	244.3	18.8	4.6	3.5	4.5	3.7
$7,000–9,999	164.2	5.7	4.7	3.5	4.7	3.6
$10,000+	142.5	4.4	5.1	4.3	5.1	4.1
All Incomes[b]			*Dental Visits*			
	273.9	19.8	1.7	0.9	1.7	0.9
Under $2,000	13.3	3.3	0.9	0.5	0.9	0.6
$2,000–3,999	22.3	3.8	0.9	0.6	0.9	0.6
$4,000–6,999	78.5	6.7	1.5	1.3	1.5	1.3
$7,000–9,999	67.4	2.8	1.9	1.7	1.9	1.7
$10,000+	79.0	2.3	2.8	2.2	2.8	2.1

[a]Age-adjusted to the civilian noninstitutional population within age groups.
[b]Includes unknown income.

Source: U.S. Department of Health, Education and Welfare, "White–Nonwhite Differentials in Health, Education and Welfare," HEW Indicators (Feb.–Oct., 1965).

was 45 per cent, approximately twice the 23 per cent
of nonwhites.

TABLE 6

Percentage of Population Making One or More
Physician or Dental Visits
July, 1963–June, 1964

Family Income	1+ Physician Visits		1+ Dental Visits	
	White	Nonwhite	White	Nonwhite
All Incomes[a]	67.4	56.2	44.6	22.7
Under $2,000	62.4	51.4	25.8	15.3
$2,000–3,999	63.5	55.6	30.5	19.9
$4,000–6,999	67.0	58.8	41.0	27.4
$7,000–9,999	70.1	63.7	52.1	32.5
$10,000+	73.1	66.6	65.1	43.3

[a]Includes unknown income.

Source: U.S. Department of Health, Education and
Welfare, "White-Nonwhite Differentials in Health,
Education and Welfare," HEW Indicators (Feb.-Oct.,
1965).

It should be particularly noted that while there
is no major difference by family income in the per
cent of the population making one or more visits to
a physician, the lowest income families have almost
three times the chronic limitation to activity than
do the highest income families.

MEDICAL CARE AND FAMILY INCOME

Of the estimated 183 million persons in the civilian noninstitutional population during the period
from July, 1962, to June, 1963, approximately 23 million (12 per cent) were living in families with incomes of less than $2,000. About 18 per cent of the
population had family incomes of $2,000 to $3,999;

34 per cent were in the $4,000 to $6,999 bracket;
and 31 per cent had incomes of $7,000 or more.*

The 23 million persons living in families with
less than $2,000 annual income were rather evenly
distributed among the age groups, with roughly one
fourth in each of the age groups--under fifteen,
fifteen to forty-four, forty-five to sixty-four, and
sixty-five years and over. Probably the most marked
differences in population by family income are those
by race. In the lowest family income interval (under
$2,000), 72 per cent of the population was white and
28 per cent nonwhite. As income level increased,
the proportion of nonwhite persons decreased; 96 per
cent of the people living in families with incomes
of $7,000 or more were white and 4 per cent nonwhite.
It is interesting to note in passing that there is a
high correlation between family income and educational level of the family head.[10]

The percentage of persons who have hospital or
surgical insurance coverage is closely related to
family income, ranging from 34 per cent among those
in families of less than $2,000 income to almost 90
per cent for persons in families of $7,000 or more
annual income. Persons of all ages in lowest income
groups and older persons in higher income groups have
least health insurance coverage (not including Medicare).

Only 22 per cent of children in low-income families have hospital insurance coverage, resulting
mostly from the low insurance coverage in large families. Possibly as a result of differences in occupation, family size, or education, nonwhite persons of
low income have a substantially lower proportion of
health insurance coverage than white persons.

---

*The remaining 5 per cent includes persons with
unknown amount of income. The 1965 census data show
the distribution of family income to be essentially
unchanged.

Although various demographic characteristics in-
fluence the rate of health insurance protection, the
greatest single factor appears to be the ability of
the family to pay for such insurance. Where the family income is over $7,000, more than 70 per cent of
the persons have hospital insurance coverage.

In the living civilian noninstitutional population of the United States, the rate of discharge from
short-stay hospitals is somewhat lower among persons
with an annual family income of less than $2,000 than
among those with higher incomes.[10] These rates, adjusted for age, were about 117 and 129 per 1,000 population for the respective income groups. During the
year, a larger proportion of persons who live in low-
income families had multiple hospital episodes than
those in higher income groups.

The average length of hospital stay decreased
from 10.7 days per person in the lowest income families to 8.7 days among persons of $2,000-3,999 family
income and 7.2 days in the income group $4,000-6,999;
the length then increased to 8.0 days per person in
the highest income group. Among persons of less than
$4,000 family income, about 33 per cent of the hospi-
tal stays were for one to three days, whereas among
those of higher incomes, 36 per cent were for one to
three days. At the other end of the scale, about 15
per cent of those with income of less than $4,000 and
about 9 per cent of those with higher income had hospital stays in excess of two weeks.

The proportion of hospital discharges that have
involved surgical procedures is less among persons of
low income than among persons of high income. For
certain selected operations--tonsillectomies, appen-
dectomies, hemorrhoidectomies, and hysterectomies--
the rate of hospital discharges is about 50 per cent
higher among persons of $4,000 or more income than
among those of lower income. However, for hernia
operations and normal deliveries, hospital discharge
rates were higher in the low-income group. For all
of these conditions except hysterectomies, the average length of post-hospital convalescence (that is,
the time required before return to normal daily

activities) was longer for persons with family incomes of less than $4,000 than for persons with high-
er family incomes.

Among persons who were hospitalized, insurance
paid for some part of the bill for about 40 per cent
of patients with less than $2,000 family income, 60
per cent of patients with $2,000-3,999 family income,
and 80 per cent of patients with higher incomes. Insurance paid three fourths or more of the bill for
approximately 27 per cent, 44 per cent, and 61 per
cent of these respective income groups. Preliminary
data from the current survey year show, for the proportion of bills for surgery or delivery paid by insurance, an even more marked association with income.
Insurance paid some part of the bill for surgery or
delivery for only 40 per cent of the surgically
treated among those with income less than $4,000,
while for persons of more than $4,000 family income,
the rate paid was 75 per cent.

Rates of disability days are inversely related
to the amount of family income, even with adjustment
for differences in the age distribution within income
intervals.[10]

Based on unadjusted data, a person with a family
income of less than $2,000 has, on the average, six-
teen days or more per year of restricted activity
than a person with an income of $7,000 or more. Com-
parable differentials were seven additional days of
bed disability and four days more lost from work.
The rate of days lost from school was fairly constant
for all income levels.

The number of disability days attributable to
chronic illness and impairment was highest among persons with a family income of less than $2,000, and
decreased consistently with higher levels of income.
Disability days associated with acute illness or in-
jury remained fairly constant regardless of amount of
family income. The relatively higher rate of disability days due to chronic illness in the lowest income
group is influenced to some extent by the comparative-
ly high proportion of older persons in this group.

The New York City Department of Health documented
the bleak relationship between poverty and wealth.
A comparison of the death rate by cause between the
low-income and high-income districts of the city
showed these rates for the following specific causes:
tuberculosis among the wealthy, 4.1 per 100,000,
among the poor, 22.5; diabetes, 17.1 for the wealthy,
30.4 for the poor; pneumonia and flu, for the wealthy,
33, for the poor, 66.2. The overall death rate of
those of high income was ten, for those of low income,
thirteen.[11]

PERSONAL HEALTH EXPENSES

Based on data collected by the health-interview
survey during the period July-December, 1962, on the
average a person in the United States spent $129 per
year for hospital care, medical and dental services,
medicines, and other health-related services or products.[10] Expenditures per person ranged from $112 for
people living in families with less than $2,000 family
income to $153 per person for those in families with
incomes of $7,000 and over.

In each of the family income intervals--under
$2,000, $2,000-3,999, $4,000-6,999, and $7,000 and
over--amounts spent for doctors' services comprised
about a third of the total health expenditures.

The health expense ($104) for a child living in
a three-member family with an income of $7,000 and
over was five times greater than the amount spent for
health care of a child in a family with seven or more
members and an income of less than $2,000.

About 18 per cent of the population had no expenses for health care or services during the twelve-
month period. This proportion varied from 11 per cent
among persons with family incomes of $7,000 and over
to 30 per cent for persons with family incomes of less
than $2,000.

At all income levels, the amount of health expenses increased with advancing age and was greater

for females than for males. In families with incomes of less than $2,000, the amount of expense
ranged from $29 per person under fifteen years of age
to $162 per person sixty-five years and older; with
family incomes of $7,000 or more, comparable amounts
were $80 per person under fifteen years of age and
$308 per person sixty-five years of age and older.

SOCIAL COSTS OF CHRONIC ILL HEALTH

After considering the foregoing health indicators,
particularly chronic health conditions causing a limitation in activity, a reasonable question might be,
"What does chronic ill health cost the nation in lost
income?" Computation of social costs of this type
are often criticized because of the inherent impre-
cision in forecasting the future return on a present
investment. However, it is considered that, given
known health conditions, it is possible to derive a
conservative dollar value that most reasonable and
knowledgeable persons would regard as a probable lower
boundary on cost of ill health to American society.

What is the loss in income due to the health differences between family units having an income of
$2,000 and less and family units having an income of
$7,000 and more? Or, stated another way, "How much
personal income would be generated by increasing the
health of the 23 million persons belonging to family
units having an income of $3,000 and less to the
equivalent health of persons belonging to family units
having an income of $10,000 or more?"

In order to answer this question, the following
four-step procedure is used to establish a conservative estimate of income forgone by the $3,000 and
under family income group because of chronic health
conditions:

    (1) A total of 3.9 per cent are unable to carry
        on major activity* and 10.7 per cent are

---

    *Major activity is defined as the ability to
work, keep house, or go to school.

limited in amount or kind of major activity. This latter percentage has been
estimated to result in approximately a
53 per cent reduction in level of major
activity.[3] The total reduction in the
ability of persons in this low-income
group to engage in any major activity
can be computed as follows:

$$[.039 + (.107) (.53)] \ 20,582,000 =$$
$$1,764,000 \text{ persons.}$$

(2) Of these 1,764,000 persons unable to car-
ry on major activity, approximately 54 per
cent, or 953,000 persons, are in the
seventeen-to-sixty-four-years age bracket.

(3) Of these persons, all healthy males and
approximately 35 per cent* of the females
would be eligible for work,[12] or

$$(953,000) \ (.50) + (953,000) \ (.50)$$
$$(.35) = 743,000 \text{ persons.}$$

Thus, approximately three quarters of a
million persons are removed from the po-
tential work force because of chronic
health conditions.

(4) In order to reflect the generally lower
skill and hence lower income-producing
capacity of the $3,000 and under income
group, the 1966 per capita income**
(rather than average worker's wage) or
$2,966 is used to compute the social cost
as follows:[12]

$$(743,000) \ (\$2,966) = \$2.2 \text{ billion.}$$

_____

*About 35 per cent of the eligible female popu-
lation is employed outside the home.

**The data were collected during the 1965-66 period

Thus, a very conservative estimate of the personal income lost by the nation due to chronic ill health is $2.2 billion.

In similar fashion we can compute (using the same four steps as above) the income loss that would result should this group have a level of health equal to that of people in the $10,000 and above family income bracket.

(1) $[.013 + (.041) (.53)]$ 20,582,000
        = 700,000 persons unable to
        engage in major activity.

(2)   700,000 $(.54)$ = 378,000 persons in the
        seventeen-to-sixty-four age bracket
        unable to engage in major activity.

(3) $(378,000) (.50) + (378,000) (.50) (.35)$
        = 255,000 persons still removed
        from the work force under improved
        health conditions.

(4) $(255,000) ($2,966)$ = $.8 billion lost
        income.

This $.8 billion represents the income that would still be lost if the health of persons in the $3,000 and under income group was improved to equal the health of persons in the $10,000 and over income group.

From the foregoing analysis we can conclude that at least $1.4 billion in personal income is lost due to the difference in health between the $3,000 and under and $10,000 and over family income groups. Or, put another way, if the health of this low family income group were improved to equal that of the $10,000 and above family income group, an increase in at least $1.4 billion dollars in personal income would probably result.

NOTES

1. U.S. Department of Health, Education and Welfare, Public Health Service, "Current Estimates from the Health Survey, United States, July 1966-June 1967," Public Health Service Publication No. 1,000, Series 10, No. 43 (1968).

2. U.S. Department of Health, Education and Welfare, Public Health Service, "Limitations of Activity and Mobility Due to Chronic Conditions, United States, July 1965-June 1966," Public Health Service Publication No. 1,000, Series 10, No. 45 (1968).

3. U.S. Department of Health, Education and Welfare, Public Health Service, "Chronic Conditions and Activity Limitations, United States, July 1963."

4. U.S. Department of Health, Education and Welfare, "Medical Care and Family Income," HEW Indicators (May, 1964).

5. U.S. Department of Health, Education and Welfare, Trends (1966-67 Edition), Part I, National Trends.

6. E. Hyck, "White-Nonwhite Differentials: Overview and Implications," paper delivered to Population Association of America, New York (April 30, 1966).

7. U.S. Department of Health, Education and Welfare, "Mortality of White and Nonwhite Infants in Major U.S. Cities," HEW Indicators (June, 1965).

8. U.S. Department of Health, Education and Welfare, "White-Nonwhite Mortality Differentials in the United States," HEW Indicators (June, 1965).

9. U.S. Department of Health, Education and Welfare, "White-Nonwhite Differentials in Health, Education and Welfare," HEW Indicators (February-October, 1965).

    10.   U.S. Department of Health, Education and
Welfare, Public Health Service, "Medical Care, Health
Status and Family Income, United States," Public
Health Service Publication No. 1,000, Series 10, No.
9 (1964).

    11.   Ingraham Hollis, Commissioner of New York
State Department of Health, "The Health Manpower
Crisis," Employment Service Review, Vol. 5, No. 5
and 6, p. 28 (U.S. Department of Labor, 1968).

    12.   U.S. Bureau of the Census, Statistical Ab-
stracts of the United States, 1968 (Washington, D.C.:
U.S. Government Printing Office, 1968), p. 315.

CHAPTER 3   MANPOWER AND WAGES IN THE HEALTH INDUSTRY

A dramatic transformation of manpower requirements is taking place in the health industry. This
transformation, including a massive expansion of the
work force and changes in technology and in the employment and occupational patterns of the work force,
has introduced new strains on the nation's health
services.

The health service industry has grown in recent
years to employ a total of approximately 3.5 million
persons in all types of health-related activities.
Payroll employment within the establishments of this
industry (hospitals, nursing homes, doctors' offices,
commercial laboratories) has risen from 1.7 million
in 1950 to more than 2.6 million in 1966.[1] These
figures do not include doctors and dentists who are
self-employed in private practice, workers such as
drugstore pharmacists who may be classified in retail
trade, government employees, and other categories.

Doctors, dentists, and nurses account for a little more than 1 million of the total. The remaining
group, totaling some 2.5 million, is composed mainly
of about 800,000 practical nurses, attendants, and
nurse's aides; several hundred thousand technicians
and therapists skilled in X-ray and laboratory procedures, rehabilitation treatments, and other specialties; and a wide range of support personnel concerned
with record-keeping, administration, food handling,
supplies, housekeeping, and related tasks. These
workers range from those in unskilled jobs to highly
skilled professionals.

PHYSICIANS

As of December 31, 1967, there were 308,630 doctors of medicine (M.D.'s) and 13,415 doctors of osteopathy (D.C.'s) in the United States, a total of 322,045 physicians. The total number of physicians per 100,000 total population increased from 149 in 1950 to 158 in 1967. The ratio of nonfederal physicians providing patient care (that is, physicians in office practice or hospital-based practice) was 130 per 100,000 civilians in 1967, up from 125 per 100,000 population in 1963. The number of nonfederal physicians providing patient care in office-based practice has declined from 109 per 100,000 population in 1950 to 100 per 100,000 in 1967. The number of physicians, total and in private practice, and the number of physicians per 100,000 population (total and civilian) are shown in Table 7. The variation of all nonfederal physicians and those in private practice per 100,000 civilians in 1967 is shown for each state in Table 1 in Appendix A. As can be seen from this data, the northeastern states generally have the highest ratio of physicians to population, and the southern states have the lowest.[2]

Fewer than two out of three physicians are in private practice, and the proportion has been dropping. Relatively more M.D.'s are in internship and residency training or operate full time in other forms of practice such as hospital service, teaching, preventive medicine, and research. However, it should be noted that these physicians often treat patients. The type of practice of physicians for selected years in the 1950-65 period is shown in Table 2 in Appendix A.

Specialists outnumber general practitioners about two to one among the active M.D.'s. In 1965, of the 244,063 physicians (M.D. and D.O.) in private practice (excluding training programs), 160,659 had a primary specialty other than private practice. However, in 1963 only slightly more than half of these specialists held certificates awarded by the American Specialty Board. A breakdown of the type of practice and primary specialty of physicians for 1965 is presented in Table 3 in Appendix A.

TABLE 7

Physicians in Relation to Population,
Selected Years, 1950-67

Year	Population in Thousands Total	Number of Physicians M.D. and D.C. All Physicians (active and inactive)	Physicians per 100,000 Population
1967	203,708	322,045	158
1966	201,585	313,559	156
1965	199,256	305,115	153
1964	196,856	297,136	151
1963	194,169	289,190	149
1960	185,369	274,834	148
1955	170,499	255,211	150
1950	156,472	232,697	149
	Civilians	Nonfederal Physicians Providing Patient Care	
1967	199,783	260,296	130
1966	197,662	254,396	129
1965	195,833	250,208	128
1964	193,612	244,542	126
1963	190,892	237,673	125

Source: U.S. Department of Health, Education and Welfare, "Health Manpower and Health Facilities, 1968," Public Health Service Publication No. 1,509 (1968).

A license to practice medicine is required
throughout the United States, which, in turn, requires graduation from an approved school, passing
an examination, and, in more than one half the states,
serving a one-year hospital internship. There are
eighty-nine medical schools and five osteopathic
colleges in the United States and Puerto Rico. Almost without exception these institutions have four-
year courses of study. In 1966-67, the ninety-four
schools enrolled 35,186 students and graduated 8,148
physicians. The number of students and graduates of
medical schools and osteopathic colleges for the
1949-67 period is shown in Table 8.

It should be noted that training a physician
takes at least eight years after graduation from high
school, and usually extends from ten to fifteen years.
The sequence is generally as follows: four years of
college work, four years of medical school, one
year's internship in an approved hospital, and two
to four years' residency training in a specialty,
followed by two or more years of supervised practice
in the specialty.

In recent years graduates of foreign medical
schools have been serving as interns and residents
in the United States. These foreign medical-school
graduates account for about 25 per cent of all physicians in training programs. The 292,100 M.D.'s in
the United States as of December 31, 1965, included
about 6,000 graduates of Canadian medical schools and
38,500 graduates of other foreign schools. Comparative data for 1959 indicate that of the recent additions to the supply of physicians in the United
States, relatively more are now foreign trained.

LICENSURE OF FOREIGN-TRAINED PHYSICIANS

Agencies in the United States concerned with medical qualifications of graduates of foreign medical
schools look to certification by the Educational Council for Foreign Medical Graduates as evidence that
the recipients of such certification have medical
knowledge at least comparable with the minimum expected

TABLE 8

Medical and Osteopathic Schools, Students, and Graduates,
Selected Years, 1949-50 Through 1966-67

Academic Year	Medicine			Osteopathy		
	Schools	Students	Graduates	Schools	Students	Graduates
1966-67	89	33,423	7,743	5	1,763	405
1965-66	88	32,835	7,574	5	1,681	360
1964-65	88	32,428	7,409	5	1,661	395
1963-64	87	32,001	7,336	5	1,594	354
1962-63	87	31,491	7,264	5	1,581	362
1961-62	87	31,078	7,168	5	1,555	362
1960-61	86	30,288	6,994	6	1,944	506
1959-60	85	30,084	7,081	6	1,915	427
1954-55	81	28,583	6,977	6	1,867	459
1949-50	79	25,103	5,553	6	1,778	373

Sources: Council on Medical Education, Education Number, Journal of the American
Medical Association, Vol. 202, No. 8 (Nov. 20, 1967), and prior annual issues;
L. W. Mills, Educational Supplement No. 18 (preliminary) (Chicago, Office of
Education, American Osteopathic Association, Jan., 1967), and prior annual issues;
U.S. Department of Health, Education and Welfare, "Health Manpower and Health Facilities,
1968," Public Health Service Publication No. 1,509 (1968).

of graduates of approved medical schools in the
United States and Canada. Such certification is considered as evidence of the quality of medical training offered by the medical school attended by the
holder of a certificate at the time of his graduation.

Medical licensure in the United States is a "state
right" and is entirely under the jurisdiction of the
governments of the individual states.[3] The power to
license physicians is exercised through the medical
licensing board of each state. The current requirements for foreign-trained physicians seeking medical
licenses in the United States and possessions is detailed in Table 4 in Appendix A, which shows the following facts of interest:

(1) Forty-one state boards require foreign-
    trained physicians to serve an internship
    of one year or more in an approved hos-
    pital in the United States before being
    eligible for licensure.

(2) Twenty-one state boards require full U.S.
    citizenship, and twenty-two state boards
    require a declaration of intention to be-
    come a U.S. citizen.

(3) All require a written examination except
    three states, which do not accept foreign-
    trained physicians for licensure at all.

(4) All but ten boards require the applicant
    to present certification obtained after
    passing an examination given by the Educa-
    tional Council for Foreign Medical Grad-
    uates.

In 1965, forty-eight state boards in the United
States examined a total of 3,011 medical-school graduates from 275 foreign medical schools.[4] The number
who were successful was 2,043; failures numbered 968,
or 32.1 per cent. Of those graduates tested in 1965,
more than 938 were from seven schools. These schools
and the results of the tests for graduates of these
schools are shown in Table 9.

TABLE 9

1965 Examination by U.S. State Boards
of Graduates of Seven Foreign
Medical Schools

Medical School	Examined	Passed	Failed	Failed (Per Cent)
Universidad Nacional de Buenos Aires	82	62	20	24.4
Universidad de la Habana, Cuba	358	226	132	36.9
National University of Athens	82	41	41	50.0
Regia Universita de Bologna, Italy	86	43	43	50.0
University of Santo Tomas, Manila	155	107	48	31.0
University of Instanbul, Turkey	96	54	42	43.8
National University of Mexico, Mexico City	79	54	25	31.7

Source: State Board Number, Journal of the American Medical Association, Vol. 196, No. 10 (June 7, 1966).

Perhaps the most interesting aspect of these statistics is presented in Table 10, giving the number of

TABLE 10

Examination of Physicians Trained in Countries
Other Than United States and Canada, 1935-65

Year	Number Examined	Passed	Percentage Failed
1935	437	303	30.7
1936	568	382	35.0
1937	920	637	30.8
1938	1,164	716	38.5
1939	1,691	839	50.4
1940	2,088	948	54.7
1941	1,717	698	59.2
1942	1,630	890	45.4
1943	1,031	518	49.8
1944	691	325	53.0
1945	475	209	56.0
1946	495	221	55.3
1947	601	283	52.9
1948	639	311	51.3
1949	737	319	56.7
1950	799	359	55.0
1951	1,006	524	47.9
1952	1,208	648	46.3
1953	1,463	796	46.3
1954	1,642	943	42.6
1955	1,771	1,042	41.4
1956	1,783	1,012	43.2
1957	2,299	1,345	41.5
1958	2,567	1,518	40.9
1959	2,766	1,870	32.4
1960	2,864	2,013	29.7
1961	2,683	1,890	29.0
1962	2,960	1,980	33.1
1963	2,781	1,861	33.1
1964	3,246	2,215	31.8
1965	3,011	2,043	32.1
Total	49,753	29,658	40.4

Source: State Board Number, Journal of the American Medical Association, Vol. 196, No. 10 (June 7, 1966).

those graduates of foreign medical facilities of medicine who were examined for medical licensure in the
United States in a thirty-one-year period (1935-65).

During the thirty-one years from 1935 to 1965
inclusive, a total of 49,753 physicians were examined
by the state boards on the basis of credentials obtained in countries other than the United States and
Canada. Of these, 29,658 passed and were licensed.
On the average, 40.4 per cent have failed the examination during this period. This represents an average
of 957 licenses per year over this thirty-one-year
period. It must be emphasized that these data do not
include Canadian physicians seeking licensure in the
various states.

These data also show a considerable increase in
the number of physicians trained abroad who were
licensed to practice in the United States during the
six years from 1960 through 1965 inclusive. During
this period an average of 2,000 such physicians
passed the examination and were licensed. This represented a failure rate of about 32 per cent compared
to the 40.4 per cent failure rate for the entire
thirty-one-year period considered previously. The
failure rate was 13.7 per cent in 1965 for U.S.- and
Canadian-trained physicians.

The output of the ninety-four U.S. medical and
osteopathic schools was 8,148 physicians in 1967, for
an average of about eighty seven graduates per school.
A wide variance exists between schools; for example,
there were one hundred eighty-two graduates from
Indiana University and thirty-seven from Woman's Medical College of Pennsylvania.[5]

In terms of 1965 conditions of medical education
in the United States, the number of foreign-trained
(non-U.S. and non-Canadian) physicians represented the
output of twenty-four medical schools. In addition,
one hundred thirty-five Canadian physicians were
licensed to practice medicine in the United States.
Therefore, each year the United States can be considered as importing the equivalent of the output of
about twenty-six U.S. medical schools. Approximately

a 30 per cent increase in the number of medical
schools would be required if importation of foreign-
trained physicians were not permitted.

NURSING AND RELATED SERVICES

Nursing services are provided today by a wide
variety of practitioners. The registered nurse is
usually supplemented by three other general categories
of nursing personnel discussed below.

Estimates of the number of personnel employed as
of January 1, 1968, in the four nursing categories
considered here are:

(1)	Registered nurses	659,000
(2)	Practical nurses	320,000
(3)	Nurse's aides, orderlies, and attendants	800,000
(4)	Home health aides	12,000

Not included above are ward clerks, who perform much
of the record-keeping duties in hospitals.

Table 11 presents the data on the number of registered nurses in relation to population. Between
1950 and 1968, the number of employed registered
nurses increased by 284,000. However, the effect is
not as great as it appears, as the number of part-
time nurses increased at a more rapid rate than the
number of those working full time.

About two thirds of the professional nurses work
in hospital nursing, not including self-employed,
private-duty nurses. Table 12 shows the number and
percentage of professional nurses in various fields
as of January 1, 1964.

In the 1966 inventory of nurses conducted by the
American Nurses' Association there were a total of
909,131 licensed registered nurses, of which 593,694
were actively employed in nursing, 285,791 not employed in nursing, and 29,646 unaccounted for. The

TABLE 11

Professional Nurses in Relation to Population,
Selected Years, 1950-68

Year	Resident Population (in thousands)	Total	Full-time	Part-time	Nurses per 100,000 Population
1968	199,017	659,000	--	--	331
1967	196,858	640,000	--	--	325
1966	194,899	621,000	--	--	319
1964	190,169	582,000	450,000	132,000	306
1962	184,598	550,000	433,000	117,000	298
1960	178,729	504,000	414,000	90,000	282
1958	171,922	460,000	--	--	268
1956	165,931	430,000	--	--	259
1954	159,825	401,600	--	--	251
1950	150,697	375,000	335,000	40,000	249

Sources: Interagency Conference on Nursing Statistics, 1954-68 estimates; U.S. Bureau of the Census, 1950 data on nurses (adjusted); U.S. Bureau of the Census, population estimates; Current Population Reports, Series P-25, No. 361 (Feb., 1967) and No. 398 (March, 1968); U.S. Department of Health, Education and Welfare, "Health Manpower and Health Facilities, 1968," Public Health Service Publication No. 1,509 (1968).

TABLE 12

Field of Practice of Professional Nurses,
Jan. 1, 1964

Field of Practice	Number of Nurses	Per Cent of Total
Hospitals, Nursing Homes, and Related Institutions	390,400[a]	67.1
Private Practice	66,000	11.3
Office	47,000	8.1
Public Health and Schools	37,200	6.4
Occupational Health	18,700	3.2
Professional Nursing Education	17,600	3.0
Practical Nursing Education	3,100	0.5
Other Fields	2,000	0.4
Total	582,000	100.0

[a]Includes about 9,000 nurse-anesthetists.

Source: Interagency Conference on Nursing Statistics, 1964.

location of active registered nurses in relation to
population prorated for the unaccounted members of
the profession is listed by state in Table 5 of Appendix A.

A license is required to practice registered
nursing in every state, which in turn requires that
the applicant must have graduated from a nursing
school approved by the state and pass a state board
examination. There are three alternative basic programs of professional nursing: (a) three-year diploma
programs conducted by hospital schools; (b) two-year
associate-degree programs conducted in community colleges; and (c) four-year (in some cases five-year)
baccalaureate programs of study in a university. Number of schools, students, and graduates of professional nursing are shown in Table 6 of the Appendix.
In 1967-68, about 72 per cent of nurses were graduated
from diploma programs.

Practical nurses provide nursing care and treatment of patients under the supervision of a registered nurse. As shown in Table 13, practical nurses
in the United States numbered 320,000 in 1968. This
data also shows the rapid growth of this health field,
which has more than doubled since 1950. In 1966, an
estimated 151,000 were employed in registered hospitals. In 1964, there were 114,100 practical nurses
working full time and 14,700 part time in registered
hospitals.

Since 1960, licensing of practical nurses has been
provided for by law and in all states. For licensure
as a practical nurse, an applicant must be graduated
from a state-approved school of practical nursing and
pass a state board examination. Requirements for ad-
mission and programs in practical nursing schools vary
considerably among the states. Generally, applicants
are required to have completed at least two years of
high school. The training usually lasts from one to
one and a half years and may be obtained in schools
operated by the public school system or schools con-
trolled by hospitals, health agencies, or colleges.
Table 14 shows the threefold growth in the number of
practical nurse graduates that took place in

thirteen years, increasing from 7,109 in 1954 to
27,644 in 1967.

TABLE 13

Practical Nurses in Relation to Population,
Selected Years, 1950-68

Year	Resident Population (in thousands)	Total Practicing Practical Nurses	Practical Nurses per 100,000 Population
1968	199,017	320,000	161
1967	196,858	300,000	152
1966	194,899	282,000	145
1964	190,169	250,000	131
1962	184,598	225,000	122
1960	179,323	206,000	115
1950	151,326	137,500	91

Source: U.S. Public Health Service Division of
Nursing, estimates of practical nurses employed in
1967-68; U.S. Bureau of the Census data for 1950 and
1960; U.S. Bureau of the Census, population estimates;
Current Population Reports, Series P-25, No. 361
(Feb., 1967) and No. 389 (March, 1968); U.S. Department of Health, Education and Welfare, "Health Manpower and Health Facilities, 1968," Public Health
Service Publication No. 1,509 (1968).

Approximately 500,000 persons were employed as
auxiliary nursing workers in hospitals and nursing
homes in 1966, in such positions as nurse's aides,
orderlies, and attendants. Based on American Hospital
Association data, 221,100 were employed as attendants
in 1950 and 375,000 in 1960.

Auxiliary nursing workers usually receive on-the-
job training; however, there are no definite educational requirements. The total number of home health
aides and homemakers has increased from about 500

employed in 1950 to 2,300 in 1960, and probably ex-
ceeded 12,000 in 1968. These workers are generally
recruited from among persons who have had little
formal education and no health training.

TABLE 14

Programs of Practical Nurse Training,
1953-54 Through 1966-67[a]

Academic Year	Reporting Programs	Graduates
1966-67	1,130	27,644
1965-66	1,018	25,688
1964-65	941	24,331
1963-64	881	22,761
1962-63	810	19,621
1961-62	707	18,106
1960-61	660	16,635
1959-60	632	16,491
1958-59	595	14,573
1957-58	511	12,407
1956-57	432	10,666
1955-56	396	10,641
1954-55	361	9,694
1953-54	290	7,109

[a]Data for United States, Puerto Rico, and other out-
lying U.S. areas.

Source: American Nurses' Association, "Facts
About Nursing: A Statistical Summary" (New York, published annually).

WAGES AND WORKING CONDITIONS IN
HEALTH INSTITUTIONS

Low wages and poor working conditions predominate
in the health industry. These two fundamental industrial characteristics prevent successful competition
of the health industry with other industries for manpower.

Administrators of health institutions regularly complain about manpower shortages and the high rate of labor turnover. Under present working conditions, it is generally agreed that the industry will not be able to attract and keep enough workers to meet its needs. As wage conditions now stand, health employees are in effect being asked to subsidize the industry. There is discontent reported throughout the industry in both technical and professional occupations. There exists obvious ferment among nurses.

The cause of much of this discontent among nurses as well as among the vast numbers of unskilled and semiskilled workers in the industry, and which may be the main reason for manpower problems, is obvious from the wage data.[6] These relatively recent data clearly establish that wages in both hospitals and nursing homes are not only low in comparison with other industries, but are pitifully substandard by any reasonable measure of income.

The average hourly earnings (cash wages) of employees in nongovernmental hospitals by selected occupation and by region are shown in Table 15. The average hourly earnings in cash wages in six selected occupations in nursing homes and related facilities is shown in Table 16. The full impact of these wage data can best be appreciated by comparison with other industries.

Table 17 shows comparative average earnings for four selected occupations in hospitals and in industry. But these averages do not tell the entire story. In hospitals in mid-1963, over 25 per cent of the registered nurses were earning less than $80 per week. The average annual earnings of nurses in metropolitan-area hospitals was $4,450, which is about $2,000 less than the average teacher's salary. Nearly 30 per cent of the hospital clerical staff were earning less than $60 per week; about 32 per cent of the nurse's aides and practical nurses were earning under $50 per week; about 40 per cent of the service workers (laundry, kitchen, and janitorial) were earning less than $48 per week (on a forty-hour basis).

TABLE 15

Average Hourly Earnings of Nongovernmental Hospital Employees
by Occupation and Region, Mid-1963

Occupation	United States	Northeast	South	North-central	West
General Duty Nurses	$2.15	$2.13	$1.93	$2.20	$2.29
X-ray Technicians	2.05	2.07	1.91	2.04	-2.24
Clerks, Payroll	1.88	1.92	1.74	1.86	2.05
Stenographers, Technical	1.92	1.92	1.76	1.91	2.14
Switchboard Operators	1.56	1.63	1.30	1.60	1.69
Switchboard Operators, Receptionists	1.45	1.40	1.30	1.40	1.74
Transcribing Machine Operators, Technical	1.72	1.75	1.56	1.69	2.05
Dishwashers, Machine	1.18	1.22	.92	1.23	1.46
Electricians, Maintenance	2.45	2.42	2.35	2.59	2.72
Engineers, Stationary	2.56	2.57	2.26	2.56	2.78
Finishers, Flatwork, Machine	1.18	1.24	.88	1.25	1.44
Housekeepers, Chief	2.45	2.59	1.96	2.57	2.62
Kitchen Helpers	1.19	1.24	.89	1.24	1.43
Maids and Porters	1.23	1.28	.89	1.29	1.51
Nurse's Aides	1.56	1.61	1.35	1.61	1.72
Practical Nurses	1.56	1.61	1.35	1.61	1.72
Washers, Machine	1.45	1.47	1.14	1.50	1.74

Source: U.S. Bureau of Labor Statistics, "Industry Wage Survey, Hospitals, Mid-1965," Bulletin No. 1,409.

TABLE 16

Average Straight-time Hourly Earnings of Employees in Nursing Homes
and Related Facilities by Region and Selected Occupations
April, 1965

Occupation	United States	Northeast	South	North-central	West
All Occupations	$1.23	$1.46	$0.90	$1.14	$1.44
Registered Professional Nurses	2.28	2.35	2.03	2.22	2.40
Licensed Practical Nurses	1.57	1.72	1.28	1.54	1.65
Nurse's Aides	1.06	1.28	.75	1.02	1.29
Kitchen Helpers	1.06	1.23	.76	.97	1.27
Laundry Workers	1.01	1.24	.72	.99	1.26
Maids and Porters	1.10	1.26	.76	1.04	1.31

Source: U.S. Bureau of Labor Statistics, "Industry Wage Survey, Nursing Homes
and Related Facilities, April 1, 1965," Bulletin No. 1,492.

TABLE 17

Average Earnings for Selected Occupations
in Hospitals and Industry
Mid-1963

Occupation	Hospitals	All Industries
Registered Nurses (per week)	$86.50	$102.50
Stenographers (per week)	77.50	89.00
Switchboard Operators (per week)	63.00	73.00
Janitorial (per hour)	1.30	1.87

Source: U.S. Bureau of Labor Statistics, "Wages
and Related Benefits, 82 Labor Markets, 1962-63,"
Bulletin No. 1,345-83.

The situation is worse in nursing homes. In
nursing homes in April, 1965, registered nurses were
averaging just over $90 per week; nurse's aides were
averaging $1.03 per hour; practical nurses were aver-
aging $1.57 per hour; porters were averaging $1.09
per hour; and laundry workers were averaging $1.00
per hour. In fact, 30 per cent of all nonsupervisory
workers in nursing homes earned less than $1.00 per
hour. Over 33 per cent of the service and maintenance employees in nursing homes were scheduled for
more than 40 hours per week, although only 20 per cent
of workers in this industry are employed in establishments that have formal provisions for the payment of
an overtime premium wage.

Fringe benefits are also poor. In nongovernmental hospitals, 50 per cent of the nonprofessional,
nonclerical employees receive six paid holidays or
fewer per year. In nursing homes, 62 per cent of
service and maintenance employees received not one
full day paid holiday during the year, while only 10
per cent received more than six paid holidays. Relatively low earnings and lack of promotion opportuni-
ties, often combined with difficult working conditions

and inconvenient working hours, help explain the fan-
tastically high rate of labor turnover in the health
industry. It is estimated that the annual turnover
rate is 60 per cent for nurses, 70 per cent for
nurse's aides, and 35 per cent for practical nurses.

It is expected that the extension of the Fair
Labor Standards Act to workers in health institutions
will have a beneficial effect. However, as shown in
Table 18, not until 1971 will the minimum wage for
hospital workers be $1.60 per hour. An estimated 16
per cent (or 237,000) of the employees in nonfederal
hospitals, nursing homes, and homes for the aged now
earn less than $1.00 per hour. This act also contains
provisions for payment for overtime work.

TABLE 18

Set Minimum Wages for Hospital Workers

Minimum Wage (per hour)	Effective Date
$1.00	February 1, 1967
1.15	February 1, 1968
1.30	February 1, 1969
1.45	February 1, 1970
1.60	February 1, 1971

Source: Amendment to the Fair Labor Standards
Act (Sept., 1966).

There are two disparities existing in the health
industry, each with broad ramifications. First, there
is the disparity between low wages and the stringent
demands made upon nonprofessional health workers.
Second, there exist no "career ladders" in the health
industry. This lack of opportunity for advancement
causes dead-end jobs. The by-products of this com-
bination are a tremendous labor turnover, manpower
shortages, and economic waste.

The health industry has a traditional "pecking
order." From the viewpoint of a nurse's aide, no

matter how experienced she may be, becoming a licensed practical nurse is as remote as for her to
become an M.D. To become a licensed practical nurse,
she must leave her job (which is usually not possible
unless personal economic resources are available),
attend a certified school, and pass a state board
examination. No credit is given for her experience
or capabilities. If she does become a licensed practical nurse and aspires to become a registered nurse,
she must begin all over again. The institutional
training for a licensed practical nurse is worthless
in becoming a registered nurse. This situation con-
stitutes a continued impediment to easing the shortage of nurses.

It would seem that the establishment of career
ladders would prove beneficial to this industry by
allowing vertical mobility. This is particularly
important for the poor without skills who may have
ability but are financially unable to leave their jobs
and return to school. It is typical that only the
poor and unskilled are willing to take jobs that keep
them in poverty.

NOTES

1. W. Mirengoff, "Health Manpower, An Emerging
Challenge," Employment Service Review (November, 1966).

2. U.S. Department of Health, Education and Welfare, "Health Manpower and Health Facilities, 1968,"
Public Health Service Publication No. 1,509 (1968).

3. Journal of the American Medical Association,
State Board Number, Vol. 192, No. 10 (June 7, 1965).

4. Journal of the American Medical Association,
State Board Number, Vol. 196, No. 10 (June 6, 1966).

5. Journal of the American Medical Association,
Education Number, Vol. 202, No. 8 (November, 1967).

6. U.S. Bureau of Labor Statistics, Bulletin No.
1,409, "Industry Wage Survey, Hospitals, Mid-1965"
(this survey covers all hospitals except those operated by the federal government).

4

HEALTH FACILITIES AND CONSTRUCTION COSTS

GENERAL HOSPITAL BEDS

In recent years the general hospital has become the focal point for the care of practically all types of patients. Historically, general hospitals have concentrated on care of the short-term acute patient. However, in the last ten years many have been adding organized units for the care of chronically ill patients as well as diagnostic and short-term care for psychiatric aid.

A general hospital is defined as follows:

> Any hospital for inpatient medical or surgical care of acute illness or injury and for obstetrics, of which not more than 50 per cent of the total patient days during the year are customarily assignable to the following categories of cases: epileptic, mentally deficient, mental, nervous and mental, and tuberculosis.[1]

In 1967, there were a total of 8,200 hospitals in the United States, with approximately 1,600,000 beds. Of these, 6,661 were nonfederal general hospitals with a total capacity of 796,140 beds. However, the number of acceptable* general hospital beds was

---

*State inventories distinguish between facilities that conform to minimum federal standards relating to construction and patient safety and those which do not.

only 503,934 in the same year, or an average of 259
acceptable general hospital beds per 100,000 population. The distribution of general hospital beds by
state is shown in Appendix B, which includes data on
the number of existing acceptable beds as well as
the total number of beds needed.

Nationally, existing general hospital beds are
equivalent to an average of 409 per 100,000 population. However, there is a large variance state by
state throughout the nation. For instance, between
1948 and 1965, although the population of the south-
eastern region increased by about one third, the number of acceptable hospital beds more than doubled,
which in turn brought about the significant increase
of 121 beds per 100,000 population in that region.
Conversely, the growth of population in the Rocky
Mountain area (coupled with a more rigid application
of standards of acceptability) caused a reduction of
55 beds per 100,000 population.*

Table 1 in Appendix B shows the variance in general hospital beds, including the number existing and
needed by states.

As of January, 1967, the Public Health Service
reported that an additional 329,997 beds were required
to bring the number of existing acceptable beds in
the United States to within the minimum limits established by the Hill-Burton Plan. It should be noted
that 292,206 hospital beds--37 per cent of the total
number of beds in the country--are designated as below minimum standards, primarily on the basis of fire
and safety hazards.[1]

---

*A ratio of 450 beds per 100,000 state population
(except 500 where state population density is from
six to twelve persons per square mile and 550 where
below six persons per square mile) was established
as the maximum bed-population ratio allowable for as-
sistance under the Hill-Burton Program for federal-
supported hospital and medical facilities construction. There are certain modifications to this limit
for unassigned reserve beds.

LONG-TERM-CARE HOSPITALS

Long-term-care hospitals fall into two categories: the chronic disease hospital, designated for
the treatment of chronic illness including degenera-
tive diseases, and nursing homes, operated for the
accommodation of convalescents or other persons not
acutely ill nor requiring hospital care, but who do
require skilled nursing care and related facilities.
The term "nursing home" is restricted by definition
to those facilities that provide skilled nursing care
and related medical services for a period of not less
than twenty-four hours per day to admitted individ-
uals.

Serious shortages exist in the number of long-
term medical facilities and beds available. This
situation is attributed to a variety of factors:

    (1) The increasing number of persons over
        sixty-five years of age.

    (2) Changes in illness patterns resulting
        from advances in medical technology.

    (3) Changes in the social living arrangements
        of families.

It is evident that the Congressional enactment of the
Social Security Amendment of 1965 (Medicaid) and Medicare will have a substantial impact in these areas.

The number of long-term-care beds increased by
more than 430,000 after 1957 to reach a total of
701,111 beds in 1967. However, only 450,602 of these
are considered acceptable under current rules. This
means that more than one third of the long-term-care
beds in the country have associated serious fire or
safety hazards. In 1967, there were 12,853 nonfederal
long-term-care facilities. Of these, 11,589 were
nursing homes with 604,083 beds, 1,032 long-term-care
units of hospitals with 53,185 beds, and 232 chronic
disease hospitals with 43,843 beds.

The number of long-term-care beds is perhaps most
effectively evaluated in terms of the population

sixty-five years old and older. In 1967, there were
2,461 acceptable long-term-care beds per 100,000 population sixty-five and over. However, it should be
noted that considerable variation exists between the
states. For instance, Maine has only 473 acceptable
long-term-care beds per 100,000 aged, while Minnesota
has a bed-aged population ratio of 5,421 per 100,000.

Despite the substantial increase in number of acceptable long-term-care beds, there remains an acute
need for additional beds. In 1967, the existing acceptable beds met somewhat more than one half the
total long-term-care bed needs of 850,524 to achieve
a bed-population ratio of 417 per 100,000.[1] This requires a net addition of 149,413 to the total existing beds, not counting the 208,083 existing beds that
require replacement or modernization.

MENTAL HOSPITALS

Nationally, it is estimated that one in ten people
have mental illness sometime in life of sufficient
severity to warrant psychiatric treatment.[2] Although
the resident population in state and local mental hospitals has been decreasing steadily since 1956 (attributed to improved therapy and greater availability
of community resources), there has simultaneously been
a steady increase both in first admissions and in re-
admissions to such facilities. In 1964, there were
326 state and local public mental institutions in the
nation, of which 32 per cent were approved by the
Joint Commission on Accreditation of Hospitals.

The number of acceptable mental beds has been
increasing over the years and reached 474,139 as of
January 1, 1965. About 83 per cent of the total
567,781 mental beds were classified as acceptable
from the safety and fire hazard standpoint.

Although the number of acceptable mental beds has
been increasing over the years, the increase has
failed to keep pace with population growth. Despite
the 25 per cent increase in acceptable beds between
1948-65, there was simultaneously a 37 per cent

increase in the total population. This resulted in
a declining ratio of acceptable mental beds per
100,000 population from 275 in 1948 to 251 in 1965.

Among the various states there is considerable
variation in acceptable mental beds. For instance,
Utah had an 85 per cent decline in the number of acceptable mental beds, whereas Virginia had a 226 per
cent increase.

TUBERCULOSIS HOSPITALS

In spite of the dramatic reduction in the tuberculosis mortality rate as well as the reduction in
the incidence of new active cases by the introduction
of modern tuberculosis therapy, this disease contin-
ues to be a serious public health problem. Newly
reported active cases still number more than 50,000
annually. About 56,000 active cases are reported to
be in hospitals, with another 60,000 active cases un-
hospitalized.

New treatment patterns created by advances in
drugs and treatment technology have resulted in shorter hospital stays and increased use of outpatient
clinic services. The consequence has been a drastic
reduction in the demand for tuberculosis beds.

In 1967, there were reported a total of 46,666
tuberculosis beds in 296 nonfederal tuberculosis facilities. This compares with a record high of 102,076
tuberculosis beds in 1954. The number of beds reported as acceptable declined to a low 31,933 in 1967.
The primary reason for this decline is that many of
these beds have been put to other uses as chemotherapy
shortens the hospital stay of tuberculosis patients.
Nationally, most of the estimated need for tuberculosis beds has been met.

DIAGNOSTIC AND TREATMENT CENTERS

A diagnostic or treatment center is a facility
providing community service for the diagnosis or

diagnosis and treatment of ambulatory patients and is
usually operated in connection with a hospital. This
includes hospital outpatient departments and clinics.

Facilities for ambulatory care have expanded considerably in recent years in number and volume of
services provided, until in 1965 approximately 10 per
cent of all non-inpatient services by physicians were
being rendered in the outpatient departments of hospitals.[3] It is estimated that in 1968 the outpatient
visits in all hospitals throughout the country will
exceed 150,000,000.[1]

During the 1957-67 period the total number of
diagnostic or treatment centers increased from 3,769
to 4,993; however, of the latter figure only 3,217
were considered acceptable for long-range planning.
These figures do not include industrial clinics limited to a firm's employees, first aid centers, and
similar facilities not furnishing a community service.
In 1965, the nation had approximately twenty acceptable diagnostic or treatment centers per million population (one per 50,000). However, considerable
variation existed between states, from one center per
2 million population in Arkansas to approximately one
center per 8,000 in Minnesota.

Under the Hill-Burton Plan an additional 2,451
diagnostic or treatment centers were programmed in
addition to the 3,217 existing acceptable centers.

PUBLIC HEALTH CENTERS

Traditionally, the public health center has been
concerned with the promotion of health by control of
communicable disease, immunization services, sanita-
tion, maternal and child health, laboratories, vital
statistics, health education, and other preventive
medical services.[4]

In 1957, 2,274 of the country's 3,067 counties,
representing an estimated 88.8 per cent of the total
population, were being served by 1,435 local health
units. However, in the same year, 25 per cent of the

counties having nearly 10 per cent of the total population were still not covered by organized local health services.[5] By 1964, an estimated 2,420 counties were being served by 1,641 local health units.[6] As of January 1, 1967, the total was 1,789 public health centers, or 9.2 centers per million population. The national current need for health centers is estimated at 10.3 centers per million population, or 2,195 centers.

For the purposes of planning, public health centers are classified as primary and auxiliary, primarily based upon separation from the central administrative office.

REHABILITATION FACILITIES

As of January 1, 1967, a reported 886 rehabilitation facilities offered medical services plus psychological, social, or vocational service. Of these, 653 were classified as acceptable on the basis of fire and safety conditions. These state vocational rehabilitation agencies reported that some 150,000 persons were restored to more productive activity during the 1966 fiscal year. In addition to the rehabilitation centers, many general hospitals, treatment centers, and nursing homes are currently making some type of rehabilitation services available.

From July, 1962, through June, 1963, an estimated 22,700,000 persons of the civilian noninstitutional population reported an inability or reduced ability to perform their major activity (work, keep house, or go to school) due to chronic illness or impairment.[7] (See Chapter 2.) According to estimates of the Vocational Rehabilitation Administration, approximately 2,500,000 handicapped people fourteen years of age and older need and would benefit from vocational rehabilitation. An estimated 300,000 additional persons enter the vocationally handicapped group each year.

HOSPITAL CONSTRUCTION--PAST OUTLAYS AND COSTS

On August 18, 1964, the Hospital and Medical Facilities Amendments of 1964 were signed into law, revising the Hill-Burton Act for the construction and modernization of health facilities. This law (P.L. 88-443) authorized a total of $1,340,000 in grants and loans for a five-year program of federal aid for new construction, modernization, and replacement of hospitals, long-term-care facilities, nursing homes, diagnostic and treatment centers, and rehabilitation facilities. The specific breakdowns are as follows:

Hospitals and public health centers:	$680 million
Long-term-care facilities:	$350 million
Diagnostic and treatment centers:	$100 million
Rehabilitation facilities:	$50 million

In addition this legislation authorized funds for modernization and replacement of obsolete health facilities beginning in fiscal year 1966 and continuing through 1969. A total of $160 million is authorized for this four-year period as follows:

Fiscal Year	Millions
1966	$20
1967	$35
1968	$50
1969	$55

A 1960 survey concluded on a sampling basis by the Public Health Service showed that it would cost at least $3 billion to modernize and replace existing facilities without increasing the total number of beds. In September, 1964, the need was estimated to exceed $4 billion, with $3 billion alone required for the general hospital field.[8] (See Chapter 2.)

As of June 30, 1964, a total of 7,372 projects had been approved under the Hill-Burton Program. Of this total, 6,046 were completed and in operation.

The remaining 1,326 were under construction or in the planning stage.

The 7,372 projects were to provide 313,762 in-patient beds in hospitals and nursing homes and 2,096 other health facilities, which are broken down as shown in Table 19.

The construction of hospitals and other medical facilities has fluctuated widely during the last thirty years, as can be seen from Table 20.

The current outlay for hospital construction is slightly less than $2 billion per year. During the sixteen years from 1948 through 1963, $12.9 billion was spent on the construction of hospitals and other health facilities not including $1.2 billion for federally owned facilities (Veterans Administration and Public Health Service facilities). Of the $12.9 billion total, $8.4 billion was spent on projects without federal aid. The volume of construction without federal aid had risen $500 million before 1956 to more than double ($1,163 million) in 1966, as can be seen from Table 21. During the five-year period from 1962 through 1966, hospital construction expenditures totaled $8.5 billion, of which $2.3 billion was for public facilities and $6.2 billion for private hospitals.

The Mental Retardation Facilities and Community Mental Health Centers Construction Act of 1963 (P.L. 88-164) also provides for construction of certain types of health facilities. Appropriations of $150 million over a three-year period beginning in 1965 have been authorized for the construction of public and other nonprofit community mental health centers. In addition, the following authorizations have been made over a four-year period for construction of mental retardation facilities:

Project grants for research centers:	$26 million
Facilities to train professional and technical personnel	$32.5 million

TABLE 19

Costs of Hospital Construction, 1950–68

Calendar Year	Hospital Construction[a] (in millions of current dollars)			Construction Cost Index[c] (1957-59 = 100 Per Cent)	Total Hospital Construction (in millions of 1957-59 dollars)
	Total	Public[b]	Private		
1950	843	499	344	75.8	1,112
1951	946	527	419	81.7	1,158
1952	889	495	394	84.4	1,053
1953	686	369	317	87.1	788
1954(r)	670	333	337	87.8	763
1955	651	300	351	90.4	720
1956	628	300	328	94.8	662
1957	879	354	525	97.7	900
1958	990	390	600	99.4	996
1959	998	428	570	102.9	970
1960	1,006	401	605	105.0	958
1961	1,140	369	771	106.3	1,072
1962	1,382	397	985	108.8	1,270
1963	1,456	426	1,030	111.3	1,308
1964	1,762	471	1,291	114.6	1,538
1965	1,912	521	1,391	118.5	1,614
1966	1,955	508	1,447	123.2	1,587

aValue of new construction put in place. Construction of health-related institutions, such as nursing homes, is included.

bIncludes construction of federally owned hospitals.

cComposite construction cost index for apartments, hotels, and office buildings.

Source: U.S. Department of Commerce, Business and Defense Services Administration, monthly Construction Review and (with Bureau of Labor Statistics of the U.S. Department of Labor) Statistical Supplement, Construction Volume and Costs, 1915-56.

TABLE 20

Hospital Construction by Source of Funds, 1950-68

| | Amount ($ millions) | | | | | | Per Cent of Total Construction | | | | |
| | | | Nonfederal | | | | | | Nonfederal | | |
Calendar Year	Total	Direct Federal	Total	Without Federal Aid	Hill-Burton Sponsor's Share	Hill-Burton Federal Share	Direct Federal	Total	Without Federal Aid	Hill-Burton Sponsor's Share	Hill-Burton Federal Share
1950	843	146	611	469	142	86	17.3	72.5	55.7	16.8	10.2
1951	946	132	710	568	142	104	14.0	75.0	60.0	15.0	11.0
1952	889	113	689	554	135	87	12.7	77.5	62.3	15.2	9.8
1953	686	66	547	438	109	73	9.6	79.7	63.8	15.9	10.6
1954	670	35	584	502	82	51	5.2	87.2	74.9	12.2	7.6
1955	651	22	588	531	57	41	3.4	90.3	81.6	8.7	6.3
1956	628	37	545	469	76	46	5.9	86.8	74.7	12.1	7.3
1957	879	45	756	581	175	78	5.1	86.0	66.1	19.9	8.9
1958	990	35	842	569	273	113	3.5	85.1	57.5	27.6	11.4
1959	998	58	793	453	340	147	5.8	79.5	45.4	34.1	14.7
1960	1,006	56	793	473	320	157	5.6	78.8	47.0	31.8	15.6
1961	1,140	55	920	608	312	165	4.8	80.7	53.3	27.4	14.5
1962	1,382	55	1,157	777	380	171	4.0	83.7	56.2	27.5	12.4
1963	1,456	89	1,179	792	387	189	6.1	81.0	54.4	26.6	13.0
1964	1,762	104	1,431	961	470	227	5.9	81.2	54.5	26.7	12.9
1965	1,912	121	1,590	1,096	494	201	6.3	83.2	57.3	25.8	10.5
1966	1,955	127	1,648	1,163	485	180	6.5	84.3	59.5	24.8	9.2

Source: U.S. Department of Health, Education and Welfare, Public Health Service, based on special reports prepared by the U.S. Department of Commerce, Bureau of Census. Title VI of the Public Health Service Act, as amended (42 U.S.C. 291-291v), provides the legal basis for the Hill-Burton program. Under a variable matching formula that takes into account local need and ability to pay, federal participation may range from one third to two thirds of the total costs of constructing and equipping health and medical facilities. A current summary and analysis of the hospital and medical facilities construction program appears in Hill-Burton Program Progress Report, Public Health Service Publication No. 930-F-3, revised annually.

62

TABLE 21

Hospital Operating Costs, 1966

Types of Hospitals	Number of		Direct Operating Cost ($ billions)	Cost per Patient Day ($ per day)	Payroll Cost per Patient Day ($ per day)
	Hospitals	Beds			
Federal	425	173,000	1.633	29.69	23.96
Nonfederal	6,735	1,506,000	12.565	27.94	18.27
Short-term	5,812	768,000	10.276	48.15	29.41
Long-term	291	67,000	.427	20.59	14.39
Mental	476	639,000	1.716	8.11	6.11
T.B.	156	31,000	.147	19.16	13.36
Total of All Hospitals	7,160	1,679,000	14.198	--	--

Source: U.S. Bureau of the Census, Statistical Abstracts of the United States (Washington: Government Printing Office, 1968).

            Grants to states for
                facilities: $67.5 million

    In September, 1963, the Health Professions Educational Assistance Act of 1963 (P.L. 88-129) was passed, which authorized appropriations of $175 million for construction grants over a three-year period. The construction program is for the building of new and rehabilitation of existing facilities for schools of medicine, dentistry, osteopathy, nursing, public health, pharmacy, optometry, and podiatry. Appropriations were also authorized for student loan funds of $30.7 million up to June 30, 1966, for studies in schools of medicine, dentistry, and osteopathy.

                              NOTES

    1. U.S. Department of Health, Education and Welfare, "Hill-Burton State Plan Data: A National Summary as of January 1, 1965" (March, 1966).

    2. U.S. Department of Health, Education and Welfare, "Hill Burton State Plan Data: A National Summary as of January 1, 1965" (March, 1966).

    3. U.S. Department of Health, Education and Welfare, "Hospital Outpatient Services: Guide to Surveying Clinic Procedures," Public Health Service Publication M CBO-C-4 (1964).

    4. V. M. Hoge, "Health Centers and the Hospital Survey and Construction Act," American Journal of Public Health (December, 1948).

    5. J. C. Haldeman, "The Development of Community Health Services," American Journal of Public Health (January, 1959).

    6. U.S. Department of Health, Education and Welfare, "Directory of Local Health Units," Public Health Publication No. 118 (1964).

    7. U.S. Department of Health, Education and Welfare, "Medical Care, Health Status and Family Income:

United States," Public Health Service Publication No. 1,000 (May, 1964).

8. U.S. Department of Health, Education and Welfare, "The Hill-Harris Amendments of 1964," HEW Indicators (September, 1964).

CHAPTER **5** TECHNOLOGICAL INNOVATION
AND MANPOWER REQUIREMENTS

CHANGING TECHNOLOGY

There is no doubt that substantial advances have
been made in medical research on disease prevention
and cure as well as in improved programs for combat-
ing environmental health hazards. However, the net
effect of this action is not expected to alter greatly the kinds of health services that will be needed
in hospitals or in other patient-care facilities
during the next decade.[1]

The advances that will most affect health facilities and manpower in the next ten years are the innovations in health technology that are being designed
and adopted for use in patient-care facilities. Changes in technology affecting patient care facilities
can be divided into four groups:

1. Innovations in diagnosis and patient care.
The electronic computer is being applied to medical
research and diagnosis. Improvements in patient-care
technology include automated chemical laboratory
equipment, artificial human organs, and improved surgical techniques, all of which are well advanced. In
other areas, changes in patient-care technology are
proceeding more slowly.

2. Innovations affecting hospital supply and
services. These changes in technology include the
adoption of plastic and other inexpensive materials
for disposable items such as hypodermic needles, surgeon's gloves, surgeon's tunics, and other products
that can be thrown away after use. Improvements in
materials-handling equipment such as specialized carts,
conveyors, and pneumatic tubes are also proving significant.

3. Advances in hospital information handling.
These advances will come primarily through use of the
electronic computer. Computers are currently being
used to a limited extent to handle patient billing
and accounting as well as to control the flow of information in hospitals so that physicians have ready
access to necessary data and can transmit orders for
treatment of patients rapidly, accurately, and with
less paper work.

4. Improvements in the management and structural
design of health facilities. Advances in structural
design of hospitals can be expected to lead to more
efficient utilization of personnel, equipment, and
buildings. They involve continuing improvement both
in management and in construction of health facilities, putting into effect concepts of progressive patient care and other advances in organizing health
services. Advances in use of computers for data pro-
cessing as well as improvements in the functional
organization, management, and design of health facilities are likely to have significant effects on manpower requirements by improving productivity. However,
it is reasonable to expect that a considerable period
of time will elapse before these effects become wide-
spread in the industry.

These new technological concepts and approaches
to productivity in the industry have affected current
manpower needs and can be expected to significantly
affect the manpower structure of the industry. For
example, the number of laboratory and diagnostic X-ray
procedures per patient has been increasing, raising
demands for technicians in these fields. The ratio
of employees to hospital patients has been rising
sharply, but the average hospital stay of a patient
has been shortened and there has been a rise in outpatient care.

IMPACT OF TECHNOLOGY ON MANPOWER REQUIREMENTS

Changes in the volume of demand for health services as well as in the facilities and kinds of care

required can reasonably be expected in the next ten years. An expanded demand for laboratory tests and X-rays can be expected to result in an increased need for trained technicians. In fact, the technological composition of the industry's work force can be expected to change. Conversely, a low rate of growth can be expected for office personnel, laundry workers, and similar categories.

New jobs can be expected to appear in the health field. There will be a need for inhalation therapists and for personnel to operate and repair medical electronic equipment. Some entirely new categories of health personnel may emerge, some of which are now only in the discussion stages, such as "assistant physician."

Thus, it can be expected that changing manpower requirements in the health industry will be felt gradually. It is reasonable to expect that current workers in the industry will not suffer from technological obsolescence in the next decade.

Through the development and use of new diagnostic and treatment equipment and procedures, technological change and innovation have visibly affected the occupational structure of many jobs. The hyperbaric chamber technician, for example, may monitor a device of the general size and complexity of an iron lung, or he may operate a room-sized piece of complicated equipment in which he and the patient are confined during treatment. At the present time, the major restriction in the use of the hyperbaric chamber is reported to be the number of trained technicians available to operate it.

Another important device, the artificial kidney machine, also illustrates the changing nature of an occupation, as well as some attendant difficulties. Today, only a relatively small number of persons suffering from uremic kidney disease have access to these machines, although they provide the only successful means of treating such patients.

WHAT MANPOWER IS NEEDED IN HOSPITALS

The following comments summarized a recent report by the Hospital Council of Maryland.[2]

> The most critical shortage is for nursing personnel--schools are not producing enough nurses to meet the demand, nor is the quality of training always of the highest. The next most critical need is for laboratory personnel. Too few training programs lead to a degree and certification. The limiting factor is not the schools . . . but the ability to attract more students to these fields.

Aside from low salaries and unattractive working conditions, a number of built-in factors tend to discourage young people from going into health careers and pose problems at all levels of hospital employment.

(1) Hospitals are highly profession-oriented. To move up the promotional ladder requires completion of an educational program that may be economically impossible for many well-motivated and well-qualified employees.

(2) Hospitals are predominantly staffed by women, which contributes to labor turnover because of marriage-associated responsibilities.

(3) There is an improper utilization of personnel, particularly in nursing. It is generally conceded by state boards of nurse examiners that better utilization would do much to relieve the nurse shortage.

It is often difficult to distinguish between formal educational programs and the wide range of

in-service training programs in hospitals. The latter
are shorter, less formalized, do not lead to a degree
or certificate, are limited to hospital employees,
and often are required to enable the employee to perform his job. Such training does not lead to advancement.

The rest of nursing education in hospital schools
is being subsidized to a large extent by the hospitals. A study shows that the net cost to the hospital
per nursing student in Maryland hospital schools is
$2,500 per year.[3] In 1964, there were 2,069 students
enrolled in Maryland hospital programs, which means
that an expense in excess of $5 million is being
borne by the Maryland hospitals to train their nurses.

Recently, in order to upgrade the quality of
laboratory personnel, the American Society of Clinical
Pathologists has required three years of academic
training, one year of hospital laboratory training,
and the passing of an examination for certification.
These requirements have apparently created an inten-
sification of the manpower shortage in laboratories.
It is considered by the Hospital Council of Maryland
that "major energy must be devoted to this crisis
before it becomes a catastrophe."

PROBLEMS IN DEFINITION OF HEALTH
MANPOWER SHORTAGES

Many estimates exist of the current magnitude of
the shortage of health manpower. Different departments of the government have arrived at different
estimates. For example, the Public Health Service
in the spring of 1966 estimated a current shortage
of 125,000 registered nurses. The Employment Service
estimate of need, based on an April, 1966, job-vacancy
survey, came to only 35,000.[4]

The Public Health Service based its estimate of
shortage on a criterion of "safe and therapeutic
services," which is based upon a "desirable level" of
medical care and hospital facilities. However, the
desirable level is often in the planning stage; it is

not a count of vacant work stations. Employment Service estimates are based on unfilled jobs for which there are current work stations and for which the employer is actively recruiting.

The Employment Service considers it a shortage when hard-to-fill jobs remain vacant for a month or more despite vigorous recruitment effort; 53 per cent of the registered nurse jobs were in this category. A considerable variation exists by area, however. In Chicago, 67 per cent of job vacancies for registered nurses were hard to fill; in Los Angeles, 43 per cent were hard to fill.

On November 13, 1966, the Public Health Service released the results of a new study of health manpower supply and needs in the nation's hospitals. This revealed significant shortages in all categories of professional and technical personnel. There exists a most urgent need for 56,920 professional nurses, 14,100 licensed practical nurses, 14,200 aides and orderlies, etc. The total technical and professional personnel most urgently needed is 108,600. Also given is the total number needed to give "optimum" care, which is 275,300 technical and professional personnel. (See Appendix C.)

NOTES

1. H. Sturm, "Technology and Manpower in the Health Service Industry, 1965-1975," Employment Service Review (November, 1966).

2. Employment Service Review, "A Growing Crisis . . . Manpower in Maryland's Hospitals" (November, 1966).

3. Hospital Cost Analysis Service, Hospital Council of Maryland, Inc. (July, 1966).

4. Employment Service Review (November, 1966), p. 43.

CHAPTER **6** ESTIMATE OF HEALTH
FACILITY OPERATING
COSTS

In 1967, the nation's total expenditures for medical care were $47 billion, or 6 per cent of the gross
national product. Of this amount, $31 billion came
from private sources and $16 billion from public ex-
penditures.[1] Although private medical expenditures
were up 148 per cent since 1950, public expenditures
increased 281 per cent in the same period. The largest
part of this gain was the result of new federal Medicare and Medicaid programs.

The largest portion of all medical expenditures
in 1967, approximately $40 billion, was spent for
personal health care. Of that amount, $10 billion
came from federal funds, $3 billion from nonfederal
public sources, and almost $27 billion (68 per cent
of the total) from private sources. Expenditures for
the construction of medical facilities was $2.2 bil-
lion, and $1.5 billion was spent for medical research
in 1967.

Preliminary data currently available for fiscal
1968 show that the nation spent $53.1 billion for
medical care, an increase of 26 per cent over fiscal
1966. Since 1950, the rate of increase for medical
expenditures has been 8.5 per cent per year. In fiscal 1968, such expenditures comprised 6.5 per cent
of the gross national product.[2]

HOSPITAL OPERATING COSTS

In 1966, the latest year for which complete data
are available, the total national expenditure for
hospital care for the nation was $15.4 billion.[3] Of
this total, $13.7 billion was spent for the services

72

of nonfederal hospitals and $1.7 billion for federal
hospital care. In addition, nursing-home care expenditures were $1.5 billion.

In 1966, the direct operating costs of the nation's
7,160 hospitals with their 1,679,000 beds was reported
to be $14.2 billion. (This does not include the $2
billion cost of new construction in 1966.) The direct
operating cost of the 6,735 nonfederal hospitals was
$12.6 billion. A detailed breakdown of the 1966 di-
rect operating cost for the nation's hospitals is shown
in Table 21.

Hospital expenses are increasing at a rapid rate
and can reasonably be expected to be 1.2 times the
1966 cost by 1970.[1]

MEDICAL SCHOOL OPERATING COSTS

An illustrative budget for a four-year medical
school with an existing class of ninety-six students
is shown in Table 22. The reader should note two
facts about these data: (1) Operating costs are in
1963 dollars. Data shows that medical school operating costs have conservatively increased at the rate
of 5 per cent per year in the 1960's.[4] (2) No operating costs are included for a teaching hospital associated with the medical school. Such teaching hospitals
had operating costs of $26,697,000 per year in 1963.

DENTAL SCHOOL OPERATING COSTS

While many of the physical considerations of
dental school construction have been worked out in
detail, no detailed breakdown of yearly operating
costs is generally available.[5] In terms of 1967 dollars, an estimate of $2 million per school year is
used for government planning purposes.[6]

THE OPERATING COSTS OF NURSING SCHOOLS

There are three programs available to persons
who desire to become registered nurses.[7] The diploma

TABLE 22

Illustrative Budget for Four-year Medical School
Entering Class, 96
(1963 costs)

Departmental Instruction and Research	2,450,900	2,302,400	128,400	20,100
Postgraduate Medical Education	24,900	20,000	2,500	2,400
Library	116,150	73,400	42,000	750
Animal Care	59,950	59,800	--	150
Central Supportive Services	102,200	76,300	25,000	900
Miscellaneous Instruction and Research Expenses	62,700	53,000	9,700	--
Equipment (All Departments)	90,000	--	90,000	--
Student Health Service	12,400	8,800	3,600	--
Admissions and Student Services	44,500	43,400	--	1,100
General Administrative Services	567,160	239,700	323,360	4,100
Operation and Maintenance of Physical Plant	581,240	193,750	387,490	--
Total	4,112,100	3,070,550	1,012,050	29,500

TABLE 23

Annual Operating Budget for Diploma Program
Entering Class 64, Total Enrollment 148
(in 1963 dollars)

Item	Cost of Educational Functions	Cost of Noneducational Functions	Total Cost
Direct Costs	$136,340	$ 17,816	$154,156
Salaries	116,000	12,602	128,602
Supplies	20,340	5,214	25,554
Indirect Costs	58,200	174,574	232,774
Staff Benefits	3,956	577	4,533
Plant Operation	35,038	--	35,038
Administration	11,630	2,097	13,727
Library	7,576	--	7,576
Health Services	--	6,233	6,233
Laundry	--	5,195	5,195
Dietary	--	79,707	79,707
Residence	--	80,765	80,765
Total	$194,540	$192,390	$386,930

TABLE 24

Operating Budget for Community College Nursing Program
(in 1963 dollars)

Item	Total	General Education Costs	Nursing Education Costs
Direct Costs	$110,452	$18,740	$ 91,712
Salaries	104,821	16,821	88,000
Supplies	5,631	1,919	3,712
Indirect Costs	55,349	14,457	40,892
Staff Benefits	6,037	1,285	4,752
Plant Operation	18,106	3,705	14,401
General Institutional Administrative Expense	11,395	2,609	8,786
Library	8,407	2,835	5,572
Student Services	11,404	4,023	7,381
Total	$165,801	$33,197	$132,604

TABLE 25

Annual Operating Budget for Baccalaureate Nursing Program,
Entering Class, 240
(in 1963 dollars)

Item	Total	Arts and Sciences Cost	Nursing Department Costs
Direct Costs	$209,102	$ 72,549	$217,553
Salaries	274,178	67,778	206,400
Supplies	15,924	4,771	11,153
Indirect Costs	23,589	34,303	89,286
Staff Benefits	11,161	3,807	7,354
Plant Operation	39,407	7,304	32,103
General Institutional Administrative Expense	22,594	6,546	16,048
Library	25,736	9,182	16,554
Student Services	24,691	7,464	17,227
Total	$413,691	$106,852	$306,839

program is conducted by a single-purpose school of
nursing under the auspices of a hospital or by a
school that is independently incorporated. This program is usually three years or less in length. The
yearly operating budget shown in Table 23 is a com-
posite of thirty-one diploma programs. Salaries provide for one director, one associate director, fifteen
faculty members, one librarian, one counsellor, one
residence director, one secretary, and five clerk-
typists.

The second type of nursing program is generally
established as a department of a community college.
The yearly operating costs for a two-year associate
degree program with an entering class of sixty-four
is shown in Table 24. Salaries provide for nonnurse
faculty and the following nursing department personnel: one director, ten faculty members, one secretary, and three clerk-typists.

A nursing program leading to a baccalaureate degree is conducted by an educational unit in nursing
that is an integral part of a college or university.
The yearly operating budget shown in Table 25 is
based on an entering class of ninety-six and a total
enrollment of 240. The salaries provide for nonnurs-
ing faculty and the following nursing personnel: one
dean, twenty-seven faculty members, one secretary,
and nine clerk-typists.

                            NOTES

    1. U.S. Department of Health, Education and Wel-
fare, "Health, Education and Welfare Trends," 1966-67
Edition, U.S. Government Printing Office, Washington,
D.C. (1968).

    2. "National Advisory Commission on Health Fa-
cilities, A Report to the President, December, 1968,"
U.S. Government Printing Office, Washington, D.C.

    3. U.S. Bureau of the Census, "Statistical Ab-
stracts of the United States, 1968," U.S. Government
Printing Office, Washington, D.C.

4.   U.S. Department of Health, Education and Welfare, "Medical Education Facilities," Public Health Service Publication No. 1,180-A-1b (1964).

5.   U.S. Department of Health, Education and Welfare, "Dental School Planning," Public Health Service Publication No. 940 (1962).

6.   Private communication, Stanley Lotzkar, Chief, Resource Analysis Branch, Division of Dental Health, Public Health Service, U.S. Department of Health, Education and Welfare.

7.   U.S. Department of Health, Education and Welfare, <u>Nursing Education Facilities</u>. Public Health Service Publication 1,180-F-1b (1964).

CHAPTER 7 MINIMAL HEALTH
NEEDS--1975

The available data on the health industry, some
aspects of which have been presented in previous
chapters, are analyzed herein to answer the following
question:

What will the cost be in money, manpower,
and physical units (schools, hospitals,
etc.) to continue the present level of
medical care, with existing variations,
allowing for projected population growth
to 1975? In other words, what change in
outlay is required to keep the present
standard of medical care?

The change in composition of the health industry's
work force in view of a changing technology was pointed
out in a preceding chapter. While a changing technology can be expected to have great impact in specific
locations at particular times, the overall composition of the work force by category is not expected to
change drastically in this time period. Therefore,
generally a relatively stable composition is expected
until 1975, with the notable exception of medical research personnel.

The analysis of health-industry needs and required
investments is based upon a planning horizon terminat-
ing at the end of 1975. In many instances, current
shortages are known to exist in both health occupations
and health facilities at the beginning of this planning period. This shortage is particularly severe in
the categories of nurses and mental-hospital beds. In
computing the 1975 minimal health needs, these shortages have been rectified, at least to satisfy needs

that were considered critical in 1966.

POPULATION DATA

In order to answer the preceding question on investment in the health industry, the population in 1975 must be estimated. Herein we use the U.S. Bureau of the Census Series B projection rounded to the nearest million as follows:[1]

0 to 19 years	86 million
20 to 64 years	117 million
65 and over	21 million
July 1, 1957, total	
U.S. population	224 million

All the subsequent data in this chapter are computed on the basis of the above total population data except that of nurses, which are computed (historically) on the basis of resident population. For the purposes of this study, the 1975 projection of resident population used is the same as the projection of total population, 224 million.

PHYSICIANS AND MEDICAL SCHOOL NEEDS

In 1967, there were a total of 322,045 physicians, of which 19 per cent were inactive or otherwise not providing patient care. The total nonfederal physician work force providing care in 1967 was 260,296. (See Table 7.) Assuming a civilian U.S. population of 199.8 million in 1967, this gives a ratio of 130 total active nonfederal physicians to 100,000 civilian U.S. population. In 1975, an active nonfederal physician work force of 291,200 will be required to maintain this ratio.

It was seen in Table 8 that in 1967 the number of graduates of U.S. medical and osteopathic schools was 8,148. Assuming the same rate of increase in the number of graduates per year over the 1967-75 period as during the 1960-67 period, there would be an average

addition to the physician work force of 8,468 per
year during each of the eight years of 1968 through
1975 inclusive. In addition, it was seen that an
average of 2,000 foreign-trained physicians per year
are added to the work force, or 16,000 over the same
eight-year period. Thus we have:

322,045	Total existing physicians (1967)
+ 67,744	additions from U.S. schools
+ 16,000	licensed, foreign-trained (excluding Canada)
405,789	
- 36,000	estimated net loss due to deaths[2]
369,789	total live physicians
- 70,260	19 per cent not providing patient care
299,529	total active physicians available (including foreign-trained).

This results in a ratio of approximately 134 active nonfederal physicians providing patient care per
100,000 total population. However, note that this
increase in active physician-population ratio is
achieved by addition of 16,000 foreign-trained physicians over the eight-year period. If no foreign additions are allowed, and U.S. Public Health Service
estimates of U.S. physician graduates are used,[3] the
projected physician-population in 1975 is as follows:

305,115	Total existing physicians (1965)
85,155	PHS projected additions from U.S. schools (1965-75)
390,270	
- 44,000	net loss due to deaths
346,270	total live physicians (1975)
65,791	19 per cent not providing patient care
280,479	total active physicians (1975).

This results in approximately 125 active nonfederal
physicians providing patient care per 100,000 total
population.

The improvement in the active physician-population
ratio from 130 to 134 that will probably take place by

1975 will be attributable to the importation and licensing of 2,135 foreign-trained physicians per year
(including Canadian) in addition to the slight increase in the number of U.S. graduates. As was pointed out in Chapter 3, this is equivalent to the average
output of twenty-six medical schools. In 1966, the
actual construction cost of a new medical school per
first-year student was approximately $400,000.[4] A
first-year student is considered equivalent to a
graduate student, as the small attrition rate is made
up by additions from the two-year medical schools.
The "start up" costs for new medical schools for the
first two and one half years of operation constitute
an additional cost of $400,000 per first-year student.

Assuming that the rates of increase in health-
facility construction costs will remain the same over
the 1967-70 period as the 11 per cent increase experienced over the 1963-66 period, the capital investment
(in terms of projected 1970 costs) is $1,896 million
to construct, equip, and start up twenty-six medical
schools that will eventually provide an increased
physician output of 2,135 per year.[5] Assuming that
the cost of medical-school operation will rise at a
rate similar to that for all medical-care costs, the
medical-school operating cost data can be realistical-
ly projected in terms of 1970 costs. The yearly operating costs of each medical school (in 1970 dollars)
would be approximately 1.23 times that shown in Chapter 6.[6] The total operating cost for twenty-six medical schools would be approximately $131.5 million
per year.

DENTISTS AND DENTAL SCHOOL NEEDS

In 1967, there were 112,152 dentists in the United
States, a ratio of 56.3 dentists per 100,000 total
population.[7] In 1963, U.S. dental schools had 3,243
graduates, but the profession experienced 2,027
deaths.[8] The U.S. Public Health Service has computed
the projected 1975 supply of dentists in the United
States to be from 120,365 to 121,055, or a dentist-
population ratio of between 53.3 and 53.6.

Assuming the 56.3 ratio can be maintained in 1975, the addition to the dentist work force is projected as follows:

$$56.3 \ (2,240) = 126,112 \qquad \text{Total dentists required (1975}$$

$$\underline{-121,055} \qquad \text{maximum projected for 1957}$$

$$5,057 \qquad \text{more dentists needed.}$$

If this shortage is to be made up in ten years, an average addition of 506 dentists must be made each year. As the average graduating class of the country's forty-one dental schools (in 1963) was sixty-seven, this is equivalent to the output of eight dental schools. Thus, eight dental schools would have to be constructed and staffed in the 1970-75 period.

The experienced cost per first-year student to construct and equip a dental school (as of December 3, 1966) was $100,000.[9] Assuming that the 12 per cent attrition rate continues, about 567 first-year students would have to be accommodated by the eight schools. The capital cost in 1970 dollars to construct and equip these dental schools would be $62.9 million.

In 1966, it cost $6,000 per student per year to operate a dental school. Assuming that all attrition takes place in the first year, an average of 2,085 students would be in the eight new schools. As the operating costs can be realistically projected to be 11 per cent more in terms of 1970 dollars than in 1966, an operating cost of $13.9 million per year would prevail.

REGISTERED NURSES AND NURSING SCHOOL NEEDS

Historically, nurse-population ratios are based on resident U.S. population, which in 1968 was approximately 199 million. In this year there were a total

of 659,000 full- and part-time nurses. Based on the
last available census (1964), we estimate that 72 per
cent of the nurses, or 474,480, are full-time and the
remainder, 184,520, are part-time employees. In 1968,
there were 331 registered nurses per 100,000 resident
population, at roughly one registered nurse for each
330 people in the country. This nurse is counted as
working either full or part time at her job.

To maintain this ratio until 1975 (assuming a
resident population of 224 million), 741,440 registered nurses will be required. The estimate of the
net loss of registered nurses to the work force per
year is 24,000.[10]

The requirement of 741,440 registered nurses in
the 1975 health-industry work force seems totally in-
accurate on the basis of employment service data presented in Chapter 5 and the description of urgent
nurse requirement in hospitals. (See Appendix C.)
Rather than compute a requirement for 1975 based on
ratios that are clearly inadequate today, we will compute future needs based on an acceptable level now.

On July 1, 1966, there were 370,200 registered
nurses in hospitals and 250,800 in service elsewhere.
There were existing needs for an additional 83,300,
or a total of 453,500 nurses needed in hospitals as
of the end of 1967. A total of 640,000 registered
nurses were in the work force as of January 1, 1967.
Of these, 67.3 per cent were in hospitals, nursing
homes, and related institutions, 19.4 per cent in
private practice, and the remainder in public health,
school, occupational health, and nursing education.
Based on the preceding critical evaluation of nursing
needs, we assume that the need for registered nurses
in 1966 would have been at least 453,500 in hospitals
and 250,800 in service elsewhere, or a total of
704,300 registered nurses.

Assuming a 1966 resident population of 195 million, a ratio of 361 nurses to 100,000 resident population would be needed. If the total resident
population in 1975 is approximately 224 million,
808,640 registered nurses will be required. Subtract-
ing the 659,000 in service in 1968 and adding the

industry's net loss of 168,000 nurses that can be expected over the seven years from 1969 to 1975, we find a total need of 317,640 registered nurses to be added to the work force by the end of 1975.

In 1967, U.S. nursing schools graduated 38,237 registered nurses. Assuming this high rate could be maintained over the seven-year period 1969-75 inclusive, there would be a total of 297,920 graduates. This would still leave a net loss of 19,720 registered nurses required to maintain the needed nurse-population ratio of 361 per 100,000 in 1975.

As of 1967, there were 1,219 schools of nursing in the United States graduating 38,237 students, or thirty-one graduates per school per year. (See Table 7, Appendix A.) In order to provide the 2,817 nurses required per year for seven years, an additional ninety-one schools are needed. The estimated capital investment cost per nursing program in 1970 dollars is $1,000,000 per nursing school, or a capital investment of $91 million.*[11]

The average operating cost per nursing program in 1963 dollars was seen in Chapter 6 to be approximately $400,000. Assuming a 1.23 cost rise between 1963 and 1970 results in an estimated $492,000 operating cost per year per nursing program. Total operating costs for the ninety-one required schools would be $44.8 million per year.

OTHER HEALTH PROFESSIONS BY MAJOR FIELD**

Medical Occupations***

In 1975 there were a total of 1,282,600 people in the medical-health occupational category, of which

---

*The costs differ widely between four-year baccalaureate, two-year associate degree, and three-year diploma programs.

**Health occupations are listed by major field in U.S. Department of Health, Education and Welfare,

305,500 were physicians. The remaining 977,100, con-
stituting a ratio of 479 per 100,000 population, were
distributed by occupation as follows:

Administration	44,000
Chiropractic	18,000
Clinical laboratory services	100,000
Dietetic services	36,000
Food and drug protective services	21,500
Health education	19,800
Medical records	37,000
Occupational therapy	12,000
Pharmacy	128,000
Physical therapy	21,000
Radiologic technology	100,000
Secretarial services	250,000
Surgical aides	19,000
Social work	21,700
Speech pathology	16,000
Veterinary medicine	24,200
Vision care	40,400
Miscellaneous categories****	68,500

Although it is not possible to forecast accurately the changing composition of the specific occupational categories, the medical occupational field can
reasonably be expected to remain of major significance
relative to the four other fields discussed before.
In order to maintain the ratio of 479 medical occupations per 100,000 population in 1975, a net addition
of 95,860 personnel are required in this health field.

Manpower Source Book, Section 18, p. 14, and in
"Health Resources Statistics," Public Health Services
Publication No. 1,569 (1968), pp. 8-11.

***Excluding physicians.

****Each of these thirteen categories has less than
10,000 members.

TABLE 26

Minimum 1975 Health Manpower Needs[a]

	Minimum 1975 Need	Expected in 1975	Additional Need
Physicians Providing Patient Care	280,479	299,529[b]	0
Dentists	126,112	121,055	5,057
Registered Nurses	808,640	788,920	19,720

	Minimum 1975 Need	1967 Work Force	Net Increase Required 1967-75
Medical Occupations (Excluding Physicians)	1,072,960	977,100	95,860
Dental Occupations (Excluding Dentists)	150,080	137,000	13,080
Nursing Occupations (Excluding Registered Nurses)	1,382,080	1,136,700	245,380
Environmental Occupations	54,600	35,000	19,600
Health Research Occupations	135,520	61,600	73,920

[a]Figures given to compensate for existing shortages and population growth.

[b]Includes importation of 2,135 foreign-trained physicians each year.

Dental Occupations*

A total of 235,700 persons were employed in dental occupations in 1967, of which 98,700 were dentists. The 137,000 remaining constituted a ratio of 67 dental technicians, hygienists, and assistants per 100,000 population in 1967. To maintain this ratio in 1975 for a population of 224 million will require a net increase of 13,080 in this health field.

Nursing Occupations**

In 1967, there were 1,136,700 nonprofessionals in the nursing health occupational category. These were mostly practical nurses, aides, orderlies, attendants, home health aides, and midwives. The ratio of nonprofessional nurses to total resident population in 1967 was 557 per 100,000. However, a current need exists for 122,850 more personnel in this category to provide optimum health care. (See Appendix C.) Thus, currently to provide necessary health care a ratio of 617 nonprofessional nursing personnel per 100,000 population would be required. This results in a required net addition to this health category of nonprofessional nursing of 245,380 by 1975.

Environmental Occupations

In 1967, there were 35,000 persons in the environmental health category, mostly sanitarians and environmental engineers. During the 1960-67 period this health occupation increased personnel 1.56 times. Assuming the same rate of increase in this rapidly expanding field by 1975, a need will exist for a total of 54,600, a net increase of 19,600 personnel.

Health Research Occupations

In 1967, there were 61,600 persons occupied in health reserach, primarily in biological-physical

---

*Excluding dentists.

**Excluding registered nurses.

TABLE 27

Minimum 1975 Health Facilities and Costs

Category	1975 Additional Need	Capital Investment ($ billion)	Operating Costs ($ billion per year)
Medical Schools	26[a]	1.896	.132
Dental Schools	8	.063	.014
Nursing Schools	91	.091	.045
Total Educational Facilities		2.050	.191
General Hospital Beds	120,020	5.185	1.759
Mental Hospital Beds	520,859	16.188	1.529
Long-term-care Beds	232,969	3.673	1.620
Diagnostic Centers	1,884	1.150	--
Rehabilitation Facilities	458	.362	--
Public Health Centers	1,218	.349	--
Total Hospital and Center Facilities	--	26.907	4.908
Grand Total		28.957	5.009

[a]Medical schools required if importation of 2,135 foreign-trained physicians per year is eliminated.

sciences, biomedical engineering, and economic research. During the 1960-67 period the number of research personnel increased 2.2 times. It seems
plausible to assume that this rate of growth will be
sustained for a total number of 135,520 in medical
research by 1975. This would require a net addition
of 73,920 research personnel.

HOSPITAL NEEDS (NONFEDERAL)

In order to compute the capital investment and
operating costs for hospitals, facilities have been
separated into general hospital, mental hospital, and
long-term-care categories primarily because of variation in costs incurred between these types of facilities.

General Hospital Beds

In Chapter 4, it was shown that there were 259
hospital beds per 100,000 persons in the United States
on January 1, 1967, that conformed to minimum federal
standards. Using this ratio for the projected 224
million population in 1975 results in a requirement
for 580,160 beds to maintain the existing "conforming" general hospital beds to population ratio. Since
on January 1, 1967, there were 503,934 existing conforming beds, a net need exists for 8,469 beds per
year over the nine-year period to the end of 1975.

In the 1967 Hill-Burton State Plan Data,[12] a need
was shown for a total of 833,931 nonfederal general
hospital beds throughout the United States and terri-
tories. This results in a bed-population of 409 per
100,000. Projecting this ratio to be that required
in 1975, there is a need for a total of 916,160 general hospital beds, or a net addition of 120,020 beds.
It should be particularly noted that this does not
include modernization or replacement of the 292,206
general hospital beds that do not conform to minimum
federal standards.

The average cost for construction of a new general
hospital during the July-December, 1968, period was

approximately $40,000 per bed.[13] This cost includes
the building and fixed and movable equipment.* The
total fixed capital investment required to supply the
needed general hospital beds (allowing for a cost in
1970 dollars of 1.08 times the experienced 1968 costs)
is consequently $5,184.9 million. The operating cost
of a nonfederal short-term hospital is $48.15 per
patient day. At 76.5 per cent occupancy, the operating cost of a net addition of 120,020 beds at this
occupancy rate is $4,421,907 per day, or $1,614 million per year in 1967 dollars. Allowing for an estimated 9 per cent increase in operating cost between
1967 and 1970, the operating cost for the needed general hospital beds is $1,759.3 million per year.

Mental Hospital Beds

The 1965 Hill-Burton State Plan Data indicated a
current need for 919,307 mental hospital beds, or a
mental-hospital bed-population ratio of 486 per
100,000. However, only 474,139 acceptable beds existed, causing an existing deficit of acceptable mental hospital beds of 445,168. Assuming that the
bed-population ratio requirement does not change significantly by 1975, the projected mental-hospital bed
need is 1,088,640. As of January 1, 1965, there were
a total of 567,781 acceptable and nonacceptable
mental-hospital beds, or a required gross net addition
of 520,859 mental-hospital beds by the end of 1975.

The construction cost per mental-hospital bed was
approximately $28,000 in 1966.[14] This results in a
required total capital investment of $16,188.3 million
in 1970 dollars. The operating cost of a nonfederal
mental hospital was $8.11 per patient day at a 91 per
cent occupancy in 1967. This results in an estimated
operating cost of $1,529.3 million in 1970 dollars,
allowing for the estimated 9 per cent increase in operating costs between 1967 and 1970.

----

*Representative construction costs are from "Joint
Economic Committee of Congress State and Local Public
Facility Needs and Financing," (December, 1966).

Long-Term-Care Beds

In Chapter 4 it was shown that a need currently
exists for 149,413 long-term-care beds to bring the
nation up to 850,524 beds, or a ratio of 417 per
100,000 population. Without considering the "expected increase to the 65 year and older group taking
place at the rate of 1,000 per day,"* the need will
be 934,080 by 1975, or a net addition of 232,969
long-term-care beds. This category of bed can be
either in chronic-disease hospital long-term-care
units of a general hospital or in nursing homes. As
nursing homes comprise the majority of the beds (86
per cent), we use a cost of $14,600 per nursing-home
bed to estimate the total capital outlay for long-
term-care facilities.[15] Allowing for projected
capital-construction cost increases of 1.08 times
1968 costs, a total capital investment of $3,673.4
million is required to construct the necessary
232,969 long-term-care beds. This does not include
the costs to modernize or replace the 208,083 existing beds that do not conform to federal safety
standards. The average cost per patient day in a
long-term-care hospital is $20.59. At the experi-
enced 84.9 per cent occupancy rate, the yearly operating cost of the needed beds in 1967 would have been
$1,486.5 million per year. Allowing for a 9 per cent
increase, $1,620.3 million per year operating cost
would be incurred to operate the necessary 232,969
long-term-care beds.

Diagnostic and Treatment Centers

In 1965, there existed a need (recognized in
federal legislation) of 5,995 diagnostic and treatment centers, or 3.07 centers per 100,000 population
ratio. If this ratio is to be maintained in 1957,
6,877 such centers will be required for a net increase
of 1,884 in addition to the 4,993 currently existing.

―――――――――

*Statement of President Johnson on signing the
Hill-Harris Amendments, HEW Indicators, September,
1964, p. 1.

Although considerable variation exists between the
various centers, an average figure of $550,000 per
center can be obtained from experienced construction
costs.[15] This would have resulted in a capital outlay of $1,036.2 million in 1966. Allowing for an 11
per cent construction cost increase between 1966 and
1970, the result is a 1970 capital investment cost of
$1,150.2 million. It is estimated that 150 million
persons received outpatient treatment at these centers during 1968. However, no operating cost data
is currently available.

Rehabilitation Facilities

As of January 1, 1967, there existed 886 acceptable rehabilitation facilities along with a need for
371 additional facilities for a ratio of needed facilities of .6 per 100,000. This results in an estimated 1975 need of 1,344, or a net addition of 458.
The experienced construction costs in 1966 was
$700,000 per facility. The associated capital outlay
in 1970 would be an estimated 1.13 times the 1966
costs, or $362.3 million. In 1967, the average cost
per inpatient was $618, and $235 per outpatient.[16]
However, currently there is no exact data on the number of patients treated.

Public Health Centers

Public Health Service regulations state an average need of one public health center per 30,000 population.* Implementation of this regulation would
result in a need of 7,467 such centers by 1975. However, Hill-Burton state agencies in consultation with
the various state departments of health have deter-
mined a current national need of 3,964 centers, of
which 2,195 would be primary and 1,769 would be auxiliary. Projecting this ratio of 1.943 per 100,000
population in 1975 results in a need for 4,352 centers,

---

*Public Health Service Regulations, Part 53,
"Grants for Construction of Hospital and Medical
Facilities," PHS Publication No. 930-A-1.

or a net addition of 1,218 to the existing 3,134 centers. Although construction costs vary greatly between centers, depending on size and location, the
average experienced cost in 1968 was $292,250.[17] This
total cost projected to 1970 results in a capital investment of $384.5 million. No data on public-health-
center operating costs are currently available.

SUMMARY

The following capital outlay and operating funds
(in 1970 dollars) are required to keep the present
level of medical care in 1975, allowing for (1) population growth, (2) nonimportation of foreign-trained
physicians, and (3) elimination of the currently existing urgent shortage of nurses in the work force.
All costs are estimated in projected 1970 dollars.

(1) Physicians. Under the present program of
     gradual medical-school growth and foreign-
     trained physician licensure, a total active
     physician population providing patient care
     of 299,529 can be expected in 1975. This
     will maintain or slightly increase the 1967
     ratio of 130 active physicians providing
     patient care per 100,000 civilian population.

(2) Medical schools. In the event that the
     annual importation and licensing of foreign-
     trained physicians is eliminated, an addi-
     tion of twenty-six U.S. medical schools will
     be required to supply 2,135 physicians per
     year. This will require a fixed capital in-
     vestment of $1,896 million and operating
     costs of $131.5 million.

(3) Dentists. The present program of dental edu-
     cation will produce a dentist work force of
     121,055 in 1975, which will require an addi-
     tional 5,057 to maintain the 1967 ratio of
     56.3 per 100,000 population.

(4) Dental schools. Eight dental schools are
     required, which will necessitate an initial

capital investment of $62.9 million and op-
erating costs of $13.9 million.

(5) Registered nurses. A need exists now for
83,300 additional registered nurses. To
correct this shortage, a minimum of 808,640
nurses will be required by 1975. An addition
of 2,817 registered nurses per year above
the current rate of production will be required to make up this deficit by 1975.

(6) Nursing schools. To satisfy these needs,
ninety-one additional nursing schools are
required at a capital investment of $91 mil-
lion and an operating cost of $44.8 million.

(7) Medical occupations (excluding physicians).
By 1975, a total of 1,072,960 persons will
be required in the medical occupation categories for a net addition of 95,860 over
1967.

(8) Dental occupations (excluding dentists). By
1975, a total of 150,080 dental technicians
and workers in associated occupational categories will be needed for a net addition of
13,080.

(9) Nursing occupations (excluding registered
nurses). To satisfy existing shortages by
1975, a net addition of 245,380 practical
nurses, nurse's aides, orderlies, etc., are
required to be added to the current 1,136,700
work force in the nursing occupations.

(10) Environmental health occupations. By 1975,
an estimated need for 54,600 persons in the
expanding environmental health category will
call for an increase of 19,600 above the
1967 level.

(11) Health research occupations. A projected
addition of 73,920 research personnel for a
total of 135,520 is forecast for the rapidly
increasing health research activities of the
nation.

(12) <u>General hospital beds</u>. In order to maintain
a ratio of 409 beds per 100,000 population
in 1975, a total of 916,160 general hospital
beds will be required, or a <u>net</u> addition of
120,020. The capital cost for this net addition would be $5,184.9 million, with an
associated operating cost of $1,759.3 mil-
lion per year.

(13) <u>Mental-hospital beds</u>. By 1975, 1,088,640
mental-hospital beds will be required, or
an increase of 520,859 above the 1965 level.
The capital investment for this net addition
would be $16,188.3 million and an operating
cost of $1,529.3 million per year.

(14) <u>Long-term-care beds</u>. In 1975, a net addition of 232,969 acceptable long-term-care
beds will be required to supply the needed
934,080 long-term-beds. The capital investment required to supply these additional
beds would be $3,673.4 million, with an as-
sociated operating cost of $1,620.3 million
per year.

(15) <u>Diagnostic and treatment centers</u>. A net increase of 1,884 centers is required by 1975
at a cost of $1,150.2 million.

(16) <u>Rehabilitation facilities</u>. By 1975, a net
addition of 458 is required at a cost of
$362.3 million.

(17) <u>Public health centers</u>. A net addition of
1,218 to the currently existing 3,134 centers
will be required at a cost of $384.5 million.

The reader should note that under existing conditions of nurse-manpower utilization and productivity,
a shortage would exist in 1975 even if the hospital
construction listed in items (12) through (14) were
forthcoming. For the purposes of this estimate, it
is considered that new constructions would incorporate
provisions for increased productivity, which would to
a great extent compensate for what would be a lack of

balance between nurses and hospital beds at 1967 productivity rates.

NOTES

1. U.S. Department of Commerce, Bureau of Census, Current Population Reports, Population Estima-
tion Series P-25, No. 359 (February 20, 1967).

2. U.S. Department of Health, Education and
Welfare, Health Manpower Source Book, Section 18, p.
26.

3. Ibid., p. 38.

4. U.S. Department of Health, Education and Welfare, Medical Architectural Guide, Table 51, p. 174.

5. U.S. Department of Health, Education and
Welfare, Health, Education and Welfare Trends (1966-
67 ed.), pp. 5-56.

6. Ibid., pp. 5-40.

7. U.S. Department of Health, Education and
Welfare, "Health Manpower, United States, 1965-1967,"
Public Health Service Publication No. 1,000, Series
14, No. 1.

8. U.S. Department of Health, Education and Welfare, Health Manpower Source Book, Section 18, p. 50.

9. Private communication, Resource Analysis
Branch, Division of Dental Health Service, U.S. Department of Health, Education and Welfare.

10. U.S. Department of Health, Education and Welfare, Health Manpower Source Book, Section 18, p. 64.

11. U.S. Department of Health, Education and Welfare, Nursing Facilities Education, Appendix A.

12. U.S. Department of Health, Education and Welfare, "Hill-Burton State Plan Data: A National Summary

13.   U.S. Department of Health, Education and Welfare, "Representative Construction Costs of Hill-Burton Hospitals and Related Health Facilities, May-December, 1965."

14.   Ibid., January-June, 1966.

15.   Ibid., July-December, 1966.

16.   Private communication, Association of Re-habilitation Centers, Washington, D.C.

17.   U.S. Department of Health, Education and Welfare, Public Health Service, Health Manpower Source Book, Section 19, "Location of Manpower in Eight Occupations" (1965).

CHAPTER **8** IMPROVED HEALTH
SERVICES BY 1975

Herein we pose the following two related questions
for analysis:

(1) What is the cost of comprehensive health
service for all U.S. citizens equal to
that currently supplied for middle-class
geographic areas?

(2) What change in outlay is required to sup-
/ply all U.S. citizens with those medical
services available to a family unit with
income of $13,500 or more?

Our analysis will show that both questions can be
answered by using Westchester County, New York, as
a sample population. This county is in the New York
City standard metropolitan statistical area, and con-
tains a large middle-class population, which demands
and is able to pay for quality medical service.

Table 28 presents a compilation of comparative
income and medical service statistics for both the
United States as a whole and for Westchester County,
New York.[1,2] The data in the table are representative
of conditions as they existed in 1964 except for population, which is based on 1962 figures. The analysis
of the percentage difference is based on the following:

X = The statistics for the United States
as a whole.

△ = The percentage change in X to equal Y.

Y = The statistics for Westchester County, New
York.

Where

$$X + \triangle X = Y$$

From this simple relationship, important orders of magnitude of the difference in medical service available to the population can be derived. What is more important, these data indicate the level of health care that can be made available to a population when a society places suitable priority on its health manpower, facility, and dollar investments.

Using this relationship and the data contained in Table 28, we see that, in 1964, Westchester County had 54 per cent more physicians, 83 per cent more dentists, 134 per cent more active nurses, and 50 per cent more pharmacists than the nation as a whole. However, only 8 per cent more general hospital beds were available in Westchester County. This can be attributed to two causes: a better level of health care and the proximity of large metropolitan hospitals in Manhattan.*

In order to supply the nation in a period of eight years with health personnel equal to the ratios existing in Westchester County, the following increases in manpower and facilities as well as capital investment and operating costs (in 1970 dollars) would be required:**

    (1) <u>Physicians</u>. A total of 492,000 physicians or 398,520 active physicians providing patient care (allowing for the inactive 19 per cent) would be required. This represents

---

*Manhattan had a 1964 bed-population ratio of 1,100 per 100,00, compared to the U.S. average of 380 per 100,000.

**An eight-year planning horizon is used to make the data comparable with the investment required to maintain the current level of medical care derived in Chapter 7.

TABLE 28

Income and Medical Service Statistics,
United States and Westchester County, N.Y.

Category	United States	Westchester County
1962 Population	184,511,000	844,100
1964 Income per Household	$7,542	$13,440
1964 Income per Capita	$2,225	$ 4,005
General Hospital Beds (per 100,000)	380	410
Active Physicians (per 100,000)	142.9	219
Dentists (per 100,000)	54.1	99
Active Nurses (per 100,000)	300	434
Pharmacists (per 100,000)	66.7	111

102

an increase of 98,991 above the 299,529
estimate for the 1975 active physician
work force. To achieve this increased
output in an eight-year period would require 142 medical schools each producing
the national average of eighty-seven
graduates. At a cost of $77.256 million
to construct and start up each medical
school, a capital investment of $10,970.4
million would be required, coupled with
an operating cost of $718.1 million per
year in terms of projected 1970 costs.[3]

(2) Registered nurses. A total of 980,000
registered nurses would be required, or
191,080 in addition to an estimated 788,920
active registered nurses in 1975. Using
the national average of 31 graduates per
nursing school per year and a period of
eight years to produce these needed nurses
results in a requirement for 770 nursing
schools. At an estimated 1970 capital construction and equipment cost of $1 million
per nursing program, a total capital investment of $770 million would be required,
along with an operating cost of $378.8
million per year.[4]

(3) Dentists. An additional 104,000 dentists
would be required above the 121,055 expected
for 1975, to make a total dentist work force
of 225,055. This requires an average addition of 13,000 dentists per year for eight
years or, at the current average output of
67 dentists per school, an addition of 194
dental schools. The estimated 1970 capital
construction cost for a dental school is
$7,862 million. A total capital investment
of $1,525.2 million would be required to
supply the needed output of dentists over
the eight-year period with an operating cost
of $337 million per year.

(4) Other health occupations. In order to estimate the additions required for the major

health fields of medical, dental, and nursing
occupations, the difference in the physician
work force is used as the critical parameter.
However, the small numbers in environmental
health and research occupations makes it
impractical to estimate the needs in these
health work force categories on this basis.
Using an average of 53.5 per cent increase
in health occupations results in the following required increases by 1975:

(a) Medical occupations (excluding physicians).
    A ratio of 479 medical occupations per
    100,000 population existed in 1967 (for a
    total of 977,100 in this health field.
    A 53.5 per cent increase would require
    net addition of 517,863 for a total of
    1,494,983 personnel in medical occupations.

(b) Dental occupations (excluding dentists).
    An estimated 137,000 dental technicians
    and associated personnel were in the work
    force in 1967. A 53.5 per cent increase
    would require an addition of 72,610 for
    a total of 209,610 in this health field.

(c) Nursing occupations (exluding registered
    nurses). In 1967, 1,136,700 persons were
    in this health category. An increased
    requirement of 53.5 per cent would result
    in a needed addition of 602,451 for a
    total of approximately 1,739,151 non-
    professional nursing occupations.

HOSPITALS AND RELATED HEALTH FACILITIES

An 8 per cent increase in the acceptable bed-
population ratio represented by the existing general
hospital facilities of 410 beds per 100,000 residents
in Westchester County is rather unrealistically low.
The availability of a large number of hospital beds
in metropolitan New York City, almost three times the
national average, mitigates against the construction
of hospital facilities in adjacent Westchester County.

In order to obtain a representative figure, the increase in physician-population ratio is again used as the critical parameter. This 53.3 per cent increase over the existing hospital beds in the nation results in the following requirements for additional medical facilities:

(1) General hospital beds. A 53.5 per cent increase in the 796,140 general hospital beds available in 1967 results in a requirement for 421,954 additional general hospital beds for a total of 1,218,094. The expected 1970 capital investment cost per general hospital bed is $43,200, which results in a total capital investment of $18,228.4 million. The estimated yearly operating cost of a general hospital bed in 1970 is $14,655 per year, or an operating cost of $6,183.7 million for the required 421,954 beds.

(2) Mental-hospital beds. Approximately 303,763 additional beds would be required in mental hospitals for a total of 871,544. The estimated 1970 capital construction cost is $31,080 per bed, which results in an additional capital investment of $9,441 million at an estimated 1970 cost of $2,936 per bed per year and an operating cost of $891.8 million per year.

(3) Long-term-care beds. A 53.5 per cent increase results in a need for 375,094 long-term-care beds for a total of 1,076,205. At an estimated 1970 capital cost of $15,768 per bed, a capital outlay of $5,914.5 million is required. At an estimated 1970 yearly operating cost of $6,955 per bed, the associated operating cost for the required 375,094 long-term-care beds would be $2,608.8 million.

(4) Diagnostic and treatment centers. An additional 2,671 centers would be required at a total capital investment of $1,630.6 million.

(5) <u>Rehabilitation facilities</u>. An additional 474
    facilities would be required at a total cost
    of about $374.9 million.

(6) <u>Public health centers</u>. An additional 1,677
    centers would be required at a total cost of
    $526.2 million.

SUMMARY

The following additional capital investment is
required to increase the level of health services
for all Americans to equal that considered to be
generally available to residents of Westchester County, New York. This additional investment would also
increase the level of medical care to equal that generally available to members of family units having
incomes of $13,500 or more. The requirements are:

(1) <u>Physicians</u>. An additional 98,991 or an
    increase of 12,374 physicians per year for
    eight years, requiring an equivalent of 142
    medical schools at an initial capital in-
    vestment of $10,970.4 million, plus addi-
    tional operating costs of $718.1 million
    per year.

(2) <u>Registered nurses</u>. An addition of 23,885
    per year for eight years for a total of
    191,080 registered nurses, requiring 770
    nursing schools at a capital investment of
    $770 million with $378.8 million per year
    in operating expenses.

(3) <u>Dentists</u>. A total addition to the dentist
    work force of 104,000 or a yearly increase
    of 13,000 for eight years would result in a
    need for 194 dental schools at a cost of
    $1,525.2 million, plus $337 million per year
    in operating costs.

(4) <u>Other health occupations</u>. Using the 53.5 per
    cent physician increase as the critical para-
    meter, a need would exist for 517,863

additional personnel in medical occupations, 72,610 in dental occupations, and 602,451 in nursing occupations. All these personnel needs are in addition to required physicians, registered nurses, and dentists.

(5) Hospitals. Again using the 53.5 per cent increase in physicians as the critical parameter, the following needs can be categorized:

  (a) General hospital beds: 421,954 additional beds at a capital cost of $18,228.4 million, plus $6,183.7 million per year in operating costs.

  (b) Mental-hospital beds: 303,763 additional beds at a capital cost of $9,441 million, plus operating costs of $891.8 million yearly.

  (c) Long-term-care beds: 375,094 additional beds costing $5,914.5 million, plus $2,608.8 million yearly in operating costs.

  (d) Diagnostic and treatment centers: 2,671 additional centers at a cost of $1,630.6 million.

  (e) Rehabilitation facilities: 474 additional facilities at a cost of $374.9 million.

  (f) Public health centers: 1,677 additional centers at a cost of $526.2 million.

The total cost for schools would be $13,265 million and for hospitals and related facilities $36,116 million, or a total capital outlay of $49,381 million. The associated yearly operating cost of these units is $11,119 million per year. This represents the nation's total investment needed to bring health care facilities up to the level prevailing in Westchester County, New York, where the average family income is almost $13,000 per year.

NOTES

1. U.S. Department of Health, Education and Welfare, Public Health Service, <u>Health Manpower Source Book</u>, Section 19, "Location of Manpower in Eight Occupations" (1965).

2. American Medical Association, "Distribution of Physicians, Hospitals, and Hospital Beds in the United States" (1966).

3. U.S. Department of Health, Education and Welfare, <u>Medical Education Facilities: Planning Considerations and Architectural Guide,</u> Table 51, p. 174.

4. U.S. Department of Health, Education and Welfare, <u>Nursing Facilities Education</u>, Appendix A.

APPENDIX A

OCCUPATIONAL DATA IN HEALTH INDUSTRY

TABLE 1

Location of Nonfederal Physicians in Relation to Population,
Dec. 31, 1967

Location	Civilian Population July 1, 1967 (in thousands)	All Nonfederal Physicians[a]		Physicians Providing Patient Care[b]	
		M.D. and D.O.	Rate per 100,000 Civilians	M.D. and D.O.	Rate per 100,000 Civilians
All Locations	198,469	292,661	147	190,748	98
	195,669	290,420	148	189,637	99
Alabama	3,505	2,871	82	2,119	75
Alaska	238	177	74	134	69
Arizona	1,606	2,347	146	1,641	126
Arkansas	1,958	1,710	87	1,315	78
California	18,793	34,555	184	23,391	161
Colorado	1,927	3,685	191	2,357	168
Connecticut	2,912	5,422	186	3,287	164
Delaware	515	727	141	479	130
District of Columbia	793	3,023	381	1,451	318
Florida	5,902	9,447	160	5,522	126
Georgia	4,389	4,558	104	3,026	93
Hawaii	684	1,002	146	681	133

Idaho	695	676	97	571	89
Illinois	10,825	14,996	139	10,029	125
Indiana	4,989	5,158	103	3,978	94
Iowa	2,752	3,298	120	2,437	105
Kansas	2,255	2,680	119	1,861	106
Kentucky	3,142	3,168	101	2,231	90
Louisiana	3,622	4,095	113	2,753	103
Maine	958	1,238	129	941	114
Maryland	3,606	6,374	177	3,021	152
Massachusetts	5,387	11,195	208	6,358	181
Michigan	8,564	12,643	148	7,874	131
Minnesota	3,577	5,414	151	3,303	136
Mississippi	2,320	1,768	76	1,333	69
Missouri	4,565	6,832	150	4,354	129
Montana	691	726	105	634	97
Nebraska	1,423	1,717	121	1,269	106
Nevada	437	477	109	372	100
New Hampshire	681	964	142	651	119
New Jersey	6,947	10,041	145	7,220	133
New Mexico	985	1,050	107	773	91
New York	18,303	40,646	222	24,122	199
North Carolina	4,913	5,168	105	3,320	92
North Dakota	627	585	93	496	87
Ohio	10,437	14,760	141	9,727	129
Oklahoma	2,447	2,904	119	2,188	106
Oregon	1,994	2,935	147	2,049	128
Pennsylvania	11,612	18,728	161	12,176	143
Rhode Island	875	1,433	164	1,018	152

(Cont.)

TABLE 1 (Cont.)

Location	Civilian Population July 1, 1967 (in thousands)	All Nonfederal Physicians[a]		Physicians Providing Patient Care[b]	
		M.D. and D.O.	Rate per 100,000 Civilians	M.D. and D.O.	Rate per 100,000 Civilians
South Carolina	2,526	2,111	84	1,539	76
South Dakota	667	575	86	492	80
Tennessee	3,858	4,497	117	2,894	104
Texas	10,657	12,571	118	9,061	106
Utah	1,020	1,365	134	927	118
Vermont	416	790	190	431	149
Virginia	4,349	5,183	119	3,302	105
Washington	3,029	4,725	156	3,221	136
West Virginia	1,797	1,870	104	1,380	94
Wisconsin	4,185	5,218	125	3,643	112
Wyoming	311	322	104	285	95
Puerto Rico	2,684	2,038	76	1,077	68
Other U.S. Outlying Areas	296	203	69	34	61

[a]Excludes 27,724 federal physicians and 1,660 with addresses unknown. Includes 14,198 inactive physicians.

[b]Includes all physicians in office-based and hospital-based practice and those in training program. Excludes the following physicians by category: 11,293 on medical school faculties, 2,746 in administration, 3,352 in research, 14,198 inactive, 1,660 with addresses unknown and 776 whose status was not reported.

Source: U.S. Department of Health, Education and Welfare, "Health Resource Statistics: Health Manpower and Health Statistics, 1968," Public Health Service Publication No. 1,509 (1968).

TABLE 2

Type of Practice of Physicians
Selected Years, 1950-65

Year	Total	Private Practice	Other Practice[a]		Training[b]	Retired, Not in Practice, Or Status Not Reported
			Nonfederal	Federal		
			Number of Physicians (M.D. and D.O.)			
1965	305,115	190,748	34,713	18,934	44,276	16,444
1964	297,136	188,430	32,064	18,345	41,651	16,626
1963	289,190	184,792	29,974	18,562	39,174	16,688
1960	274,834	179,176	27,748	14,218	38,291	15,401
1955	255,211	169,871	--	--	--	--
1950	232,697	168,089	--	--	--	--
			Percentage of Physicians (M.D. and D.O.)			
1965	100	63	11	6	15	5
1964	100	63	11	6	14	5
1963	100	64	10	6	14	5
1960	100	65	10	5	14	5
1955	100	67	10	5	12	5
1950	100	72	7	6	9	6

[a]Includes full-time staff in hospital service (other than interns, residents, and fellows), full-time medical-school faculty, and physicians whose primary activity is administrative medicine, laboratory medicine, preventive medicine, or research.

(Continued)

TABLE 2 (Cont.)

b Includes federal and nonfederal interns, residents, and fellows.

Sources: A.M.A. Directory Report Service, Quarterly Tables of Distribution of Physicians by Professional Activity and by State and County (Chicago, American Medical Association, Jan. 3, 1966), Vol. 17, Sup. No. 47, also prior reports; Membership and Statistics Department, A Statistical Study of the Osteopathic Profession, Dec. 31, 1965 (Chicago, American Osteopathic Association, June, 1966), also prior editions.

TABLE 3

Type of Practice and Primary Specialty of Physicians

Primary Specialties	Number of Physicians (M.D.)					Number of D.O.'s in Private Practice
	Total Active	Private Practice	Other Practice		Training Programs[c]	
			Non-federal	Federal		
All Specialties	277,575	180,752	34,403	18,912	43,508	9,996
General Practice[a]	83,309	65,951	4,260	4,465	8,633	8,728[b]
Medical Specialties	61,860	37,408	4,671	4,671	11,277	307
Surgical Specialties	84,351	59,850	5,208	4,147	15,146	773
Psychiatry & Neurology	20,254	9,291	5,024	1,623	4,316	27
Other Specialties	27,801	8,252	11,407	4,006	4,136	161

[a] Includes no specialty and other specialties not recognized.
[b] Includes 938 with practice limited to manipulative therapy.
[c] Includes pediatric allergy and cardiology.

Source: A.M.A. Directory Report Service, Quarterly Tables of Distribution of Physicians by Professional Activity and by State and County (Chicago, American Medical Association, Jan. 3, 1966), Vol. 17, Sup. No. 47; Membership and Statistics Department, A Statistical Study of the Osteopathic Profession, Dec. 31, 1965 (Chicago, American Osteopathic Association, June, 1966).

TABLE 4

Status of Requirements for Medical Licensure
for Physicians Trained in Foreign
Countries (Other Than Canada)
1965

Location	Written Examination	Admitted Also on Reciprocal or Endorsement Basis	Citizenship	Basic Science Certificate	Internship	Certification by Educational Council for Foreign Medical Graduates	Additional Requirements	Examination Fee (in dollars)
Alabama	x	...	x	x	x	x	x	25
Alaska	x	x	x	x	x	...	...	35
Arizona	x	...	x	x	x	x	x	50
Arkansas	Not Accepted							
California	x	...	..	..	x	...	x	40
Canal Zone	x	...	..	..	x	x	x	10
Colorado	x	...	x	x	x	x	x	50
Connecticut	x	...	D	x	..	...	x	50
Delaware	x	x	x	..	x	x	x	50
District of Columbia	x	x	..	x	x	x	...	35
Florida	x	...	x	x	..	x	x	50
Georgia	x	x	x	..	x	x	x	50
Guam	..	x	..	..	..	x	...	50
Hawaii	x	...	D	..	x	x	x	50
Idaho	x	...	D	..	x	x	x	100
Illinois	x	...	..	..	x	...	x	75
Indiana	x	...	D	..	..	...	x	25
Iowa	x	x	D	x	x	x	x	50
Kansas	x	...	x	x	x	...	x	50
Kentucky	x	...	x	..	x	x	x	50
Louisiana	Not Accepted							
Maine	x	...	..	..	x	x	x	100
Maryland	x	...	D	..	x	x	x	50
Massachusetts	x	...	D	..	..	...	x	50
Michigan	x	x	D	x	x	x	x	30
Minnesota	x	...	D	x	x	x	x	50
Mississippi	x	...	x	..	..	x	x	35
Missouri	x	...	x	..	x	x	...	50
Montana	x	x	x	..	x	x	...	75

Location	Written Examination	Admitted Also on Reciprocal or Endorsement Basis	Citizenship	Basic Science Certificate	Internship	Certification by Educational Council for Foreign Medical Graduates	Additional Requirements	Examination Fee (in dollars)
Nebraska	x	...	x	x	..	x	..	50
Nevada	Not Accepted							
New Hampshire	x	x	D	..	x	x	x	50
New Jersey	x	...	x	..	x	...	x	50
New Mexico	x	...	D	x	..	x	..	100
New York	x	x	D	..	x	x	x	40
North Carolina	x	...	x	..	..	x	x	50
North Dakota	x	...	D	..	x	x	x	100
Ohio	x	x	D	..	x	x	x	50
Oklahoma	x	...	x	x	x	x	..	25
Oregon	x	...	D	x	x	x	x	150
Pennsylvania	x	...	D	..	x	x	x	50
Puerto Rico	x	...	x	..	x	...	..	30
Rhode Island	x	x	D	x	x	x	x	50
South Carolina	x	...	x	..	x	x	x	100
South Dakota	x	x	D	x	x	x	x	40
Tennessee	x	...	x	x	..	x	x	50
Texas	x	x	D	x	..	x	x	50
Utah	x	...	..	x	x	x	x	25
Vermont	x	...	D	..	x	x	..	20
Virgin Islands	x	...	..	..	x	...	x	65
Virginia	x	...	D	..	x	x	x	50
Washington	x	x	..	x	x	x	..	25
West Virginia	x	...	x	..	x	x	x	25
Wisconsin	x	...	D	x	x	x	x	75
Wyoming	x	x	x	..	x	x	..	50

Key: x = yes.
       D = Declaration of intention to become citizen
           of the United States.

TABLE 5

Location of Active Professional Nurses (1962) and Practical Nurses (1960)

Location	Resident Population Jan. 1, 1962 (in thousands)	Professional Nurses		Resident Population Jan. 1, 1960 (in thousands)	Practical Nurses	
		Number	Nurses per 100,000 Population		Number	Nurses per 100,000 Population
United States	184,598	550,000	298	179,323	205,974	115
Alabama	3,317	5,224	157	3,267	3,617	111
Alaska	242	694	287	226	118	52
Arizona	1,486	4,972	335	1,302	1,205	93
Arkansas	1,842	2,219	120	1,786	2,010	113
California	17,029	55,240	324	15,717	18,169	118
Colorado	1,893	7,005	370	1,754	2,603	148
Connecticut	2,625	11,537	440	2,535	2,800	110
Delaware	467	1,828	391	446	471	106
District of Columbia	789	4,148	526	764	1,749	229
Florida	5,434	16,432	302	4,952	5,046	102
Georgia	4,083	7,924	194	3,943	4,613	117
Hawaii	693	1,998	288	633	952	150
Idaho	700	1,932	276	667	1,017	152
Illinois	10,098	29,371	291	10,081	8,440	84

Indiana	4,663	11,575	248	4,662	3,896	84
Iowa	2,774	8,874	320	2,758	2,863	104
Kansas	2,215	6,281	284	2,179	2,527	116
Kentucky	3,084	5,382	175	3,038	2,775	91
Louisiana	3,371	6,681	198	3,257	3,521	108
Maine	978	3,630	371	969	1,548	160
Maryland	3,233	7,949	246	3,101	2,847	92
Massachusetts	5,188	26,032	502	5,149	11,339	220
Michigan	8,029	21,322	266	7,823	11,864	152
Minnesota	3,461	13,285	384	3,414	3,948	116
Mississippi	2,261	3,203	142	2,178	2,592	119
Missouri	4,316	9,505	220	4,320	5,862	136
Montana	697	2,433	349	675	742	110
Nebraska	1,446	4,624	320	1,411	1,895	134
Nevada	350	917	262	285	242	85
New Hampshire	622	3,056	491	667	922	152
New Jersey	6,357	22,101	348	6,067	4,870	80
New Mexico	997	2,126	213	951	770	81
New York	17,498	67,830	388	16,782	15,191	91
North Carolina	4,704	10,876	231	4,556	3,957	87
North Dakota	633	2,153	340	632	522	83
Ohio	10,038	29,569	295	9,706	11,615	120
Oklahoma	2,448	4,000	163	2,328	3,838	165
Oregon	1,807	6,285	348	1,769	2,656	150
Pennsylvania	11,382	42,222	371	11,319	13,125	116
Rhode Island	878	3,473	396	859	1,118	130
South Carolina	2,448	5,244	214	2,383	1,610	68

(Continued)

TABLE 5 (Cont.)

Location	Resident Population Jan. 1, 1962 (in thousands)	Professional Nurses		Resident Population Jan. 1, 1960 (in thousands)		
		Number	Nurses per 100,000 Population		Number	Population per 100,000
South Dakota	721	1,948	270	681	605	89
Tennessee	3,652	6,473	177	3,567	4,381	123
Texas	10,122	17,448	172	9,580	13,386	140
Utah	958	2,245	234	891	801	90
Vermont	387	1,722	445	390	679	174
Virginia	4,248	9,998	235	3,967	3,960	100
Washington	3,010	10,148	337	2,853	4,597	161
West Virginia	1,796	4,455	248	1,860	1,892	102
Wisconsin	4,019	13,333	332	3,952	3,503	89
Wyoming	332	1,078	325	330	245	74

TABLE 6

Schools of Professional Nursing, Students, and Graduates,
1955-56 Through 1967-68[a]

Academic Year	Schools	Students[b]	Total	Diploma	Associate Degree	Bachelor's Degree
1967-68	1,262	141,948	--	--	--	--
1966-67	1,219	139,070	38,237	27,452	4,654	6,131
1965-66	1,191	135,702	35,125	26,278	3,349	5,498
1964-65	1,153	129,269	34,686	26,795	2,510	5,381
1963-64	1,142	124,744	35,259	28,238	1,962	5,059
1962-63	1,128	123,861	32,398	26,438	1,479	4,481
1961-62	1,118	123,012	31,186	25,727	1,159	4,300
1960-61	1,123	118,849	30,267	25,311	917	4,039
1959-60	1,119	115,057	30,113	25,188	789	4,136
1958-59	1,126	113,518	30,312	25,907	462	3,943
1957-58	1,118	112,989	30,410	26,314	425	3,671
1956-57	1,115	114,674	29,933	26,141	276	3,516
1955-56	1,125	114,423	30,236	26,828	252	3,156

[a]Data for United States and Puerto Rico.
[b]Fall enrollment at beginning of academic year.

Source: American Nurses' Association, Facts About Nursing: A Statistical Summary, (New York, published annually).

121

APPENDIX B

HOSPITAL FACILITY DATA

TABLE 1

General Hospital Beds by State[a]
Jan. 1, 1967

State	Total Existing Facilities[c]	Number of Existing Acceptable Beds[b]	Existing Acceptable Beds per 100,000 Population	Total Beds Needed[d]	Total Beds Needed per 100,000 Population
United States and Territories	6,661	503,934	259	833,931	392
United States	6,532	500,622	258	825,209	394
Alabama	140	11,053	321	17,395	472
Alaska	18	270	122	592	238
Arizona	72	4,008	253	6,919	343
Arkansas	115	5,766	296	7,347	354
California	540	51,948	284	60,290	280
Colorado	83	5,948	308	9,647	430
Connecticut	35	4,746	168	10,415	335
Delaware	7	615	124	1,855	331
D.C.	14	3,668	466	5,062	580
Florida	176	17,961	314	32,486	459
Georgia	175	13,757	323	18,857	404
Hawaii	23	1,387	214	1,989	284
Idaho	50	1,239	181	2,264	301

Illinois	260	32,369	305	51,685	456
Indiana	114	9,293	191	21,372	409
Iowa	147	6,610	240	13,933	493
Kansas	155	5,145	234	10,486	463
Kentucky	138	7,862	250	11,925	365
Louisiana	140	10,844	310	14,673	377
Maine	61	2,099	215	4,164	407
Maryland	45	7,906	228	12,240	313
Massachusetts	132	10,318	194	25,388	447
Michigan	254	20,971	256	36,285	414
Minnesota	182	12,056	340	17,451	457
Mississippi	127	8,006	348	10,209	410
Missouri	166	11,482	257	21,507	468
Montana	64	1,325	190	3,311	440
Nebraska	113	3,820	262	6,577	429
Nevada	20	885	205	1,616	327
New Hampshire	30	1,578	238	2,929	405
New Jersey	106	10,573	157	25,311	337
New Mexico	48	2,534	251	3,234	275
New York	371	45,804	254	76,107	393
North Carolina	138	10,453	217	20,494	397
North Dakota	61	2,180	341	3,117	474
Ohio	215	27,923	273	43,980	397
Oklahoma	169	7,282	297	10,313	402
Oregon	84	4,717	249	6,615	324
Pennsylvania	266	26,107	227	52,894	442
Rhode Island	16	2,612	301	3,646	394

(Continued)

TABLE 1 (Cont.)

State	Total Existing Facilities[c]	Number of Existing Acceptable Beds[b]	Existing Acceptable Beds per 100,000 Population	Total Beds Needed[d]	Total Beds Needed per 100,000 Population
South Carolina	77	6,118	246	9,843	363
South Dakota	66	1,926	277	3,334	447
Tennessee	176	9,242	242	17,853	437
Texas	580	30,218	291	46,348	406
Utah	42	2,575	261	3,683	317
Vermont	22	1,240	312	1,985	446
Virginia	109	9,199	214	17,561	374
Washington	117	5,132	175	8,906	278
West Virginia	81	3,543	196	8,135	459
Wisconsin	164	15,050	364	19,426	436
Wyoming	28	1,259	376	1,555	418
Guam	1	40	59	210	268
Puerto Rico	125	3,228	123	8,230	265
Virgin Islands	3	44	102	282	477

aAs reported in the Hill-Burton Plans as of January 1, 1967.

bExisting acceptable beds include "excess" beds available in some areas; thus the sum of the ratios of existing acceptable beds plus additional beds needed exceed the bed-population ratio of total need.

cRepresents the total number of civilian general hospital facilities reported in the Hill-Burton State Plans; includes facilities that have been approved and/or scheduled for construction.

dBased on bed needs as reported in the Hill-Burton State Plans.

APPENDIX C

PRESS RELEASE--

DEPARTMENT OF HEALTH, EDUCATION AND WELFARE

U.S. DEPARTMENT OF
HEALTH, EDUCATION AND WELFARE
Public Health Service
Bethesda, Maryland 20014

FOR RELEASE   HEW-N82
Sunday, November 13, 1966

A new study of health manpower supply and needs
in the Nation's hospitals reveals significant shortages in all categories of professional and technical
personnel.

Surgeon General William H. Stewart announced today that comprehensive information on hospital manpower is now available from a study made jointly by
the American Hospital Association and the Public Health
Service.

The study was made to determine the number of personnel employed, current vacancies, and estimates of
personnel needs. Data from the first 4,600 hospitals
which reported have been used to estimate totals for
all 7,100 hospitals in the United States registered
by the American Hospital Association. These reports
indicate that the total number of professional, technical and auxiliary personnel employed in hospitals is
about 1.4 million. About 275,000 additional professional and technical personnel would be needed to provide optimum patient care, an increase of about 10
per cent over present staffing. Over 80,000 more professional nurses and more than 40,000 practical nurses
are needed. Some 50,000 aides are needed in general
hospitals; another 30,000 in psychiatric institutions.
Over 9,000 more medical technologists, almost 7,000
social workers, and about 4,000 more each physical
therapists, X-ray technologists, and surgical technicians are needed.

Most urgent needs are for nurses, practical nurses, and aides. High on the urgent list, too, are medical technologists, laboratory assistants, radio-logic technologists, dietitians, physical therapists, occupational therapists, and social workers.

A complete report of this study will be available within the next few months. Data from similar studies of manpower resources in hospitals not registered by the American Hospital Association and in nursing homes and other long-term care facilities will also be available.

TABLE 1

Hospital Personnel Needs, 1966
(HEW-N82)

Category of Personnel	Present Staff	Most Urgent Needs	Total Optimum-care Needs	
Total professional and technical[a]	1,380,800	108,600	275,300	
Professional nurses	370,200	56,920	83,300	Nurse
Licensed practical nurses	148,500	14,100	42,800	Health
Aides, orderlies, etc.	373,100	14,200	48,700	Field
Psychiatric aides	156,200	7,600	31,300	
Medical technologists	52,900	4,100	9,100	
Radiologic technologists	23,700	1,000	3,900	
Laboratory assistants	14,400	800	2,400	
Medical record personnel				
Professional	6,200	600	1,800	
Technical	10,000	300	1,800	
Surgical technicians	17,400	500	3,800	
Dietitians	12,600	1,600	3,600	
Food service managers	5,300	100	800	
Cytotechnologists	1,600	--	500	
Histologic technicians	3,900	--	600	
Electrocardiograph technicians	5,900	--	900	
Electroencephalogram technicians	1,900	--	400	

(Continued)

TABLE 1 (Cont.)

Category of Personnel	Present Staff	Most Urgent Needs	Total Optimum— care Needs
X-ray assistants	5,700	--	900
Occupational therapists	4,600	1,200	2,800
Occupational therapy assistants	5,000	--	1,500
Physical therapists	8,000	800	2,800
Physical therapy assistants	5,200	--	1,100
Speech pathologists & audiologists	1,000	--	600
Recreation therapists	4,600	100	1,900
Inhalation therapists	5,500	600	2,300
Pharmacists	9,500	600	1,900
Pharmacy assistants	5,500	100	900
Medical librarians	2,900	--	800
Social workers	12,100	2,000	6,400
Social work assistants	1,500	--	600
All other professional & technical	105,900	1,300	15,100

[a]Figures may not add because of rounding.

Source: Estimates for all registered hospitals based on PHS-AHA survey. Cols. 1 and 3 based on 4,600 returns; col. 2 based on 421 returns.

APPENDIX D

RECAPITULATION

APPENDIX D

RECAPITULATION

The U.S. Health Industry--
The Costs of Acceptable Medical Care by 1975

In order to maintain the 1968 level of medical care experienced in the United States by the year 1975 (without depleting the physician work force of other nations and eliminating existing crucial short-ages of nurses) an outlay of $29 billion in capital investment plus at least $5 billion in yearly operat-ing costs will be necessary. These funds will be required to construct and operate the facilities shown in Table 1.

It should be noted that no data are available on costs necessary to provide the required health indus-try employees who are historically trained on the job, such as technicians and aides.

In order to supply the nation in a period of ten years with health personnel and facilities to the level existing for the population of Westchester County, New York (a household income of $13,440), an outlay of $49 billion in capital investment plus at least $11 billion in yearly operating costs will be required, as shown in Table 2.

Westchester County Data

The data shown for Westchester County and United States comparison (Table 2 in Appendix D) are based on the difference in the ratio of physicians to pop-ulation. This critical parameter indicates a 53.5 per cent increase in all categories of health services required.

TABLE 1

Facilities and Costs of 1975 Medical Care
(Based on 1968 Level)

Category	Additional Number Needed	Capital Investment ($ billions)	Yearly Operating Costs ($ billions)
Medical Schools	26	1.896	.132
Dental Schools	8	.063	.014
Nursing Schools	91	.091	.045
General Hospital Beds	120,020	5.185	1.759
Mental-hospital Beds	520,859	16.188	1.529
Long-term-care Beds	232,969	3.673	1.620
Diagnostic Centers	1,884	1.150	--
Rehabilitation Facilities	458	.362	--
Public Health Centers	1,218	.380	--

Total Additional Capital Investment $28.988 billion
Total Operating Costs for Required
    Additional Units $ 5.009 billion per year

TABLE 2

Facilities and Costs of 1975 Medical Care
(Based on Data for Westchester County, N.Y.)

Category	Additional Number Needed	Capital Investment ($ billions)	Yearly Operating Costs ($ billions)
Medical Schools	142	10.970	.718
Dental Schools	194	1.525	.337
Nursing Schools	770	.770	.379
General Hospital Beds	421,954	18.228	6.184
Mental-hospital Beds	303,763	9.441	.892
Long-term-care Beds	375,094	5.915	2.609
Diagnostic Centers	2,671	1.631	--
Rehabilitation Facilities	474	.375	--
Public Health Centers	1,677	.526	--

Total Additional Capital Investment $49.381 billion

Total Yearly Operating Costs for the
Additional Units $11.119 billion

137

Westchester County Hospital Utilization*

A survey conducted on May 10, 1961, showed that
2,981 residents of Westchester County were in southern
New York hospitals; 83 per cent of these were 2,404
were in Westchester hospitals. However, Westchester
hospitals had 2,789 occupants on this day. This indicates that a differential flow (residents of Westchester in excess of Westchester beds occupied) of
6 per cent treated outside the county.

---

*Hospital Planning, for the People of Southern
New York (New York: Hospital Review and Planning
Council of Southern New York, 1964).

ABOUT THE AUTHOR

Edward Yost is an assistant professor at Long
Island University, where he teaches management engineering and operations classes in industrial
economics and production planning. He has worked
at Douglas Aircraft Company and was principal engi-
neer at Fairchild Camera and Instrument Corporation.
His previous publications include articles in Life
Magazine and Photogrammetric Engineering. He received his D.Sc. in Engineering from Columbia.